Eva Hoffman   Zdzisław Bartkowicz

THE LEARNING ADVENTURE

LEARNING SKILLS WORKBOOK FOR CHILDREN AND YOUNG PEOPLE

Illustrations by Justina Langley

LEARN TO LEARN

Cover design and illustrations by Justina Langley © 1999

ISBN: 0 9535387 0 2   (book & audio CD)

Published by:

    LEARN TO LEARN
    PO Box 29
    Middlewich
    CW10 9FN - UK
    Tel +44 (0)1606 832 895
    Fax +44 (0)1606 837 645
    learntolearn@connectfree.co.uk

Printed in England

Other titles by Dr Eva Hoffman:

The Learning Adventure - ISBN 0953538702

A Guide to The Learning Adventure - ISBN 0953538710

My First Book Of Abundance - ISBN 0953538761

For You, Dear Teacher - ISBN 0953538788

Introducing Children To... (full set of 4 titles) - Series ISBN 095353877X
    ... Mind Mapping - ISBN 0953538745
    ... Their Intelligences - ISBN 0953538729
    ... Their Senses - ISBN 0953538737
    ... Their Amazing Brains - ISBN 0953538753

We would both like to thank

The Good Fortune, which has brought us together, initiated our most inspiring, full of fun and joy, co-operation.

Martin Hoffman, for the endless hours he has devoted to the editorial work, and his wife, Sarah, for taking it so well.

Richard Kirby, Peter Wingard, and Emily Preston, for reading the manuscript, making valuable comments and suggesting changes.

Slavek Litwinski, for cooking wonderful meals and generally taking care of us while our heads were buried in the computer.

Eva would like to thank

Andrew Rzechowski, my life partner, without whose encouragement, caring, support and belief in me and in what I do, I would not have been brave enough to do many of the things I have done.

My daughter, Justina Langley, and my son, Martin Hoffman, for being most wonderfully supportive and encouraging throughout the process of putting this book together and for their invaluable input into the project. Without you two, there would be no book!

My beautiful Grandchildren, Nicola, James, Christopher and Richard Langley, and Jack and Rachel Hoffman, for teaching me what children really want and need, and for all the love they have brought into my life.

My dear friend, Richard Kirby, for his help and unfailing belief in me.

My father, Jan Hoffman, for sharing with me his precious and valuable insights into teaching (all of which are perfectly valid 40 years later!) and for equipping me for life with the courage to be different, the enthusiasm for searching for answers, the joy of life and a positive mind.

Janice Bain, for suggesting I go to the 1991 SEAL conference which has changed my life in many ways.

Grethe Hooper Hansen, for her incredibly high level of enthusiasm and for her encouragement, inspiration and support.

All my students, who have taught me so much, inspired me no end and given me lots of positive strokes. A big thank you to you all!

Zdzislaw would like to thank

My Mother, Valeria Bartkowicz, for her unfailing love, her belief in me and support in all my endeavours.

All my students, who have taught me a lot throughout the years and without whom I could never be the person I am today.

Eva Hoffman   Zdzisław Bartkowicz

THE LEARNING ADVENTURE

Illustrations by Justina Langley

contents

contents

Dear Learner,

You probably wonder whether this book is really for you. If so, find out by asking yourself this question:

Would I like to find learning easier, learn faster, get better grades, and on top of all that have a lot of fun doing it?

If the answer is 'yes', this book most certainly is for you.

To be successful at school you need to find out how you can learn best. It is just as important to know how to loosen up, how to concentrate and what to do to really believe that you can succeed.

The exercises in this book will show you how to do it. You may decide to do some of them all by yourself and others with somebody else, for example your parent, grandparent or a friend. It may be more fun to share your thoughts with another person but remember: do what feels best for you!

We have divided the exercises into five parts. Whenever you decide to have a go, do one exercise from each section. If you really want to make progress, at some point it is necessary to do all the exercises, and not just once... Some of them will need more practice.

The last page of each section deserves special attention: we ask you to choose the exercises you like best. From now on they will be your best friends, helping you with your learning whenever you need it.

We strongly believe that if you really want to, you will make big progress and surprise your parents, your teachers, and most importantly, YOURSELF!

We wish you the very best of luck.

smile at yourself

smile at yourself!

Liking yourself and believing in yourself

People who like themselves enjoy life. They attract positive and happy people who help them believe in themselves and in their ability to do well in whatever they choose to do.

People who like themselves understand how to be their own best friend, and don't behave in a self-destructive way.

Many of us don't like ourselves much and make ourselves miserable. As a result we do not like the world around us, either.

To accept yourself is the basis of success and happiness, even though there may still be many things about you you want to change.

It is worth thinking about, don't you think?

smile at yourself!

No shop sells 'like-yourself pills'. Liking yourself is something you, like everybody else, will have to work on. The most important thing is that **you can do it!**

You can develop self-esteem that will support you in life and give you a good chance for success at school and your life outside school: your relationships with your family, friends and other people around you.

Your self-esteem is affected by many things so it may go up or down. If it is healthy, it bounces back quickly; if not, it tends to stay low. The important thing is to make it bouncy.

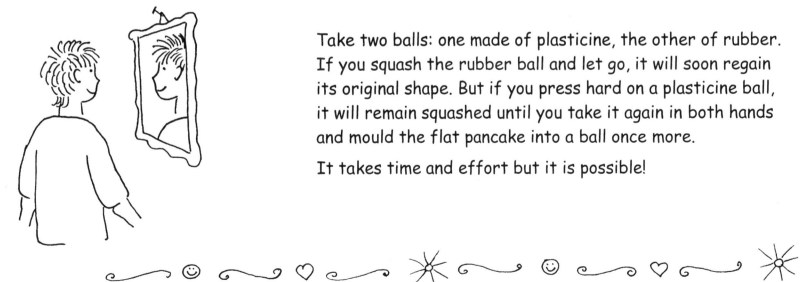

Take two balls: one made of plasticine, the other of rubber. If you squash the rubber ball and let go, it will soon regain its original shape. But if you press hard on a plasticine ball, it will remain squashed until you take it again in both hands and mould the flat pancake into a ball once more.

It takes time and effort but it is possible!

smile at yourself!

Your inner weather report

Sit still for a moment.

Breathe and observe your breath... in... out... in... out...

Place your hand on your heart...

How are you today?

Does your heart tell you anything about the way you feel?

Take an inner weather report.

Is it sunny in there or cloudy?

Drizzly or pouring with rain?

Is the air mild or is it heavy and oppresive as if you were expecting a storm?

Is it cold, warm, or hot?

Now take a sheet of paper, choose three coloured pencils or markers and draw a picture of the weather in your heart.

smile at yourself !

More about your inner weather

If there is no sun in your heart and if the picture you have drawn is rather sad, breathe in... and out... and stay for a moment with your feelings...

Now close your eyes and imagine you are floating on a raft... the lake is calm and the air comfortably warm... The raft is rocking gently as you watch the clouds go by and feel the warm breeze tickle your cheeks...

Remember the unpleasant feelings you had when drawing your picture?

Put your hands and legs into the water... now let the water wash those feelings away...

Let the breeze take the rest of them... and let the discomfort melt...

Feel the warmth of the sun in your heart.

Now open your eyes, again choose three crayons or markers and draw another picture of your heart's weather. Have you noticed any change?

YOUR INNER WEATHER DEPENDS GREATLY ON YOU

THE SUN WILL BE THERE IF ONLY YOU LET IT SHINE

Happy words, nasty words...

When people are upset, sad, disappointed or angry they often think and say nasty things about themselves:

I am ugly!

I always feel so stupid!

Nobody likes me!

I never do anything right!!!

Nobody needs me...

In fact, none of this is true. You sometimes feel stupid; some people don't like you, and from time to time you make a mess of things. Words such as 'always', 'never', 'everybody' and 'nobody' certainly sound very dramatic but they are great exaggerations.

Repeating bad thoughts about yourself, such as *I am ugly* or *I am stupid*, is much more dangerous than you think. When your mind is filled to the brim with such words, there is no space left for good thoughts.

Nasty and negative words will easily create a programme for a miserable and negative life. As you can guess, to design a programme for a happy and successful life you will need good and positive words.

smile at yourself!

Imagine your best friend phones you, evidently very angry and upset, and says:

I am really stupid... I can never do anything right!

Nobody wants to play with me...

Nothing makes sense any more... I've had enough of everything and everybody!!!

You try to tell him that it's not true but he isn't listening.

What could you do to help your friend?

Think and write down your ideas here:

smile at yourself!

What to do when your friend is down in the dumps

You could tell him that YOU like him and explain why.

You could remind her of situations when she was proud of herself.

You could suggest going for a walk to his favourite place or getting some ice-cream.

You could remind her of all the people who really care for her.

You could both listen to some music, either soothing and relaxing or completely wild. You could dance some crazy dances

together.

You could do something that will make him laugh: tell a joke, make a funny face, remind him of a funny situation.

You could tell her that you love her and will be there for her when she needs moral support.

Talk with your friends and share your ideas about what helps you when you feel bad. Sometimes the best thing is to leave people alone for a while. If you do that, remember to **say** that if they want to talk, you are always ready to listen!

Your 'liking-yourself' repair kit - the *MAGIC BOX*

Bad days happen to all of us: when they do, we are not happy with ourselves and think that nobody likes us. What is worse, we don't like ourselves! Talking to somebody who cares may help but it does not always work... Eva also had bad days, even weeks... until she came across a wonderful discovery: a self-esteem repair kit, the *MAGIC BOX!* We strongly recommend that you try it out too.

Find yourself a box. Any box will do. If it's old and scruffy, you can paint pictures on it or glue some nice coloured paper all over it to make it bright and cheerful.

Go through your drawers where you keep your treasures and put them all in your *MAGIC BOX.* Starting today, every time you get a special card, a fun photograph or any object that is special to you, put it in your box.

Keep the box in a safe place. Any time you feel sad or upset, open your box, take out your treasured possessions, look at them and remember how they came to you and what makes them special. Most likely, you will instantly feel better.

REMEMBER TO OPEN YOUR MAGIC BOX EVERY TIME YOU FEEL SAD

smile at yourself !

Words with wings

When you have many winged, uplifting words in your mind, it is as if you had a hot air balloon always ready to take you up to the sky.

Fill the balloon with words and things which can make you feel happy, energetic and ready for action.

smile at yourself!

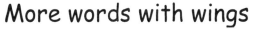

More words with wings

The more good words and thoughts we have for ourselves, the better and more confident we feel.

Practise saying them either aloud or silently to yourself and let them lift you up, especially when you don't feel too good about yourself.

On the next page complete the sentences in the balloons so that they could uplift you and give you wings.

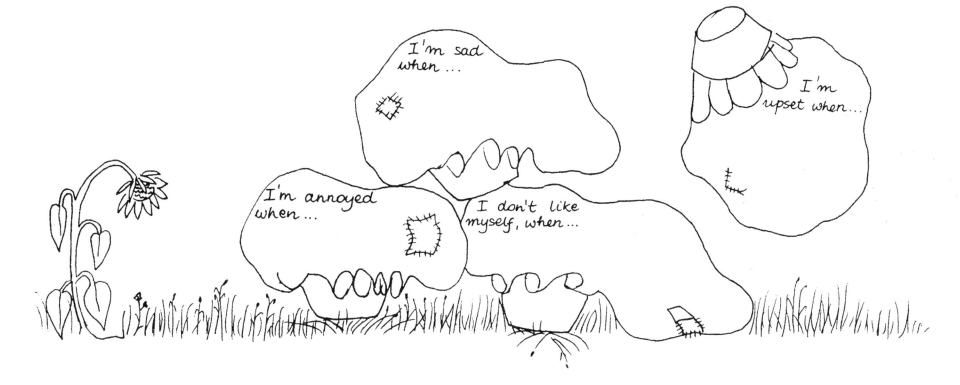

smile at yourself! ☺

☺

Not-so-good words...

Negative words and thoughts pull us down towards sadness
and disappointment.

Complete sentences in the balloons that have lost the air:

smile at yourself! ☺

☺

With what words and thoughts could you fill the balloons,
so that they could fly?

smile at yourself !

Choose your words carefully

Fill the flying balloon with words, that can help people feel good about themselves.

In this balloon write words which make you feel bad about yourself, cause anger, sadness, pain and bitter disappointment.

LEARN TO AVOID THESE WORDS!

Harmful words!!! DO NOT USE

smile at yourself!

You are absolutely unique

In many ways we are all very much alike. Our bodies are built in the same way, and we all need love. But no two people in the whole world are the same. Each of us experiences different things in life and that is why we think and feel differently.

To prove it I would like you to do an exercise. You will need to ask a few people to do it with you, whoever is available. Ask everybody to draw a heart in the middle of a page and ten lines coming out of the heart. Now ask them to write on the lines things that come into their minds when they think about **Love**. When all the lines are filled, compare the results.

You may have written a few similar things to other people's but most of them will probably be different.

This is because all people are special and unique. Isn't it wonderful?!

REMEMBER THAT YOU ARE SPECIAL AND UNIQUE

smile at yourself!

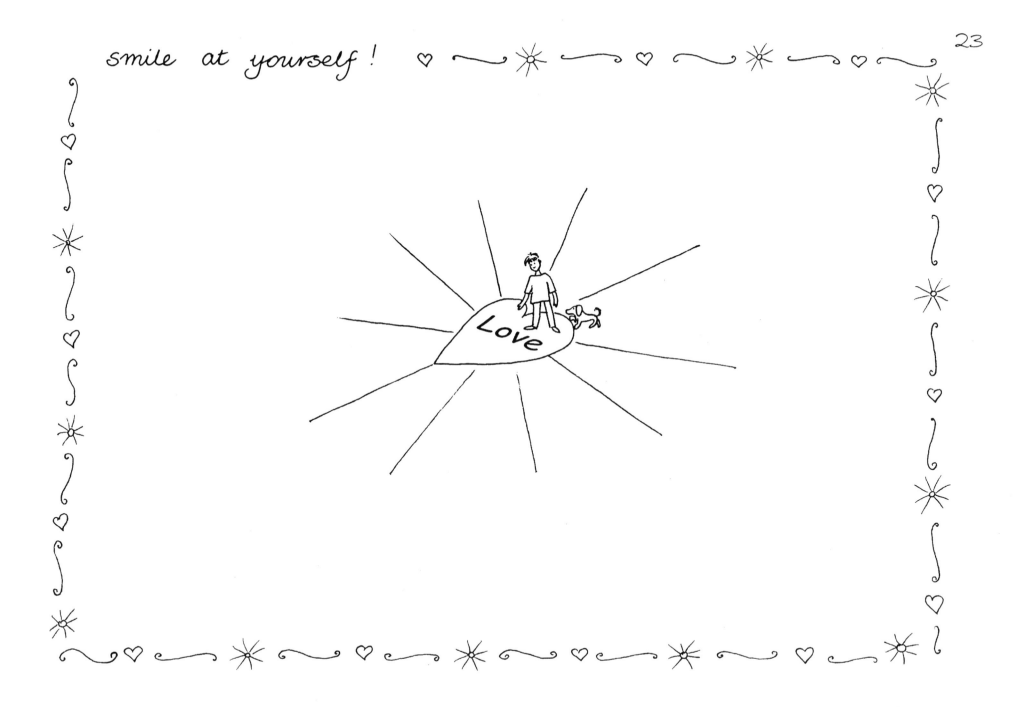

Love

Your wonderful characteristics

Can you, without giving it much thought, name at least a few of your good characteristics?

You can test yourself by quickly completing the sentences:

I am ....

I can ....

I am proud that I ....

I am good at ....

I like myself because ....

Being aware of your abilities and good points is important and necessary. You should not think it is bragging which aims at showing others that you are better than them. It's good to know what you are good at and what is good about you. This can help you achieve what you want to achieve.

Write a good thought about yourself in the speech bubble.

YOU NEED TO KNOW YOUR GOOD POINTS

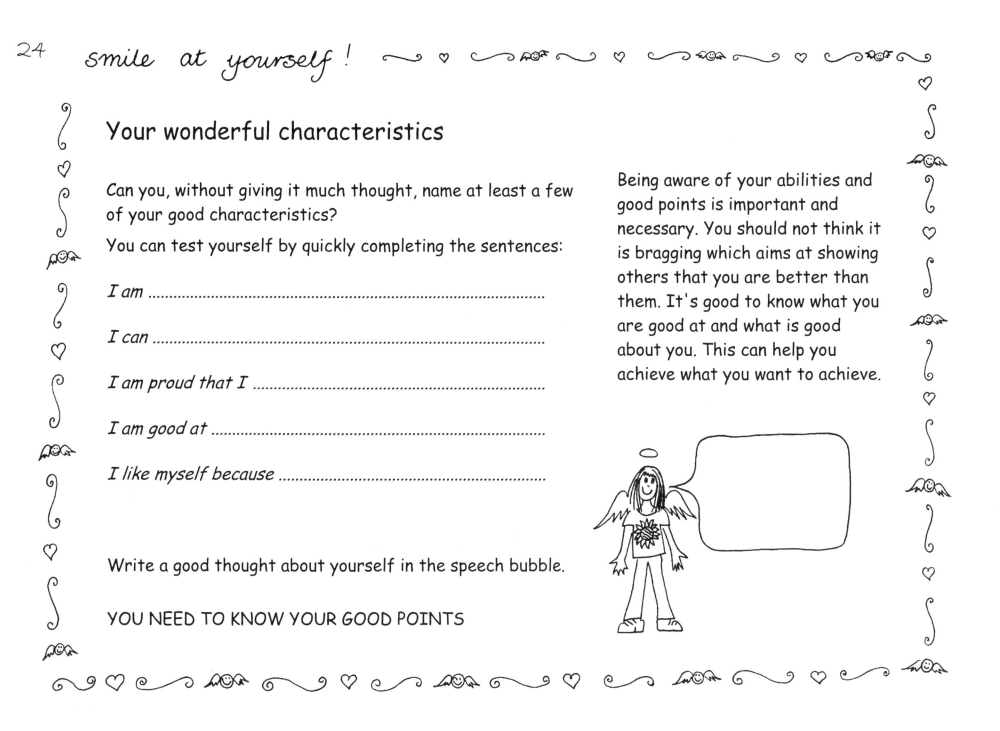

smile at yourself!

I am great!

Choose the nicest possible picture of yourself and glue it onto the sun.

On the sun's rays write all the good things about you and all the things that make you special.

If there are any rays left, write on them the characteristics you **would like** to have.

smile at yourself !

Good words for your *MAGIC BOX*

Give some coloured sheets of paper to people who know you well and care about you. Ask them to write letters to you saying what they value in you, and what they especially like about you.

After you have enjoyed
reading those letters,
put them in your
MAGIC BOX.

IF YOU WANT TO BE REALLY HAPPY YOU NEED TO APPRECIATE WHO YOU ARE
AND WHAT YOU HAVE

smile at yourself!

Your family and friends about you

your smiling picture

Glue your smiling picture in the middle frame. Ask your parents, sisters or brothers, friends, and other people who care about you to write in the empty frames what they like, love and value about you.

Good things in your life

Having something and not being able to enjoy it is worse that not having it at all.

We only seem to realise how much things meant to us when we have lost them. People who only think about what they **don't** have are miserable because they don't notice what they **do** have.

Do you ever think of the good things in your life and how much they mean to you?

Do it now. Make a list of everything you appreciate in your life. If you think about it long enough you will be surprised how long the list will be.

....

....

....

....

APPRECIATION IS THE KEY TO HAPPINESS

smile at yourself!

More good things in your life

Keep adding to the list whenever you remember something more.

....

....

....

....

....

....

REMEMBER THAT APPRECIATION IS THE KEY TO HAPPINESS

Be your own best friend

Everybody is good at some things but no-one needs to be good at everything.

This is true about you, too.

Perhaps, like most people, you always compare yourself with others.

You see that Kelly has better grades; Andy has been abroad on holiday; Chris has a new computer, while Sophie has nicer clothes and speaks French really well.

Comparing yourself with others is quite natural. It's fine if you come to the conclusion that you are different from others, but then, so is everybody else! Or, you may be inspired to get better at doing something. However, if your conclusion is that you are not as good as others, you could easily get very upset, maybe even depressed.

You have **value as yourself**. It does not depend on your grades, new clothes, long legs, or sporting achievements. Do not destroy it by comparing yourself with others and judging yourself down.

Rather than being your judge, be your own best friend!

In the first column write your most important strengths

And here write your best friend's most important strengths

....

....

....

....

....

....

No matter what your strengths are, you are neither better nor worse: you are simply different.

CELEBRATE THE DIFFERENCES BETWEEN YOURSELF AND OTHER PEOPLE

smile at yourself!

Strengths and weaknesses

Everybody has strong and weak points; it's a fact of life. Whenever you compare yourself with somebody else try to think about all the parts of your personalities.

You may find that Brian is a better swimmer than you but that you make fewer spelling mistakes.

Danielle has more friends but you wouldn't dream of exchanging all of them for your wonderful friend Molly.

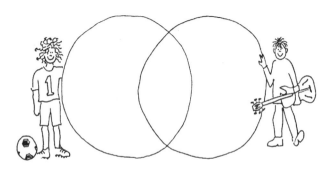

smile at yourself!

Think about the strengths and weaknesses of your best friend and yourself and write them in the circles. Where the circles overlap, write the characteristics which you have in common.

IT IS GOOD TO NOTICE AND ACCEPT DIFFERENCES BETWEEN PEOPLE

smile at yourself!

Labels, labels, labels...

People address others using all sorts of descriptive words, as if they wanted to stick labels on them. Some labels such as 'funny', 'beautiful' or 'speedy' are good: they may even help a person believe in himself or herself. However, most labels do harm because they hurt and destroy confidence. The worst thing about labels is that once they stick to a person, they remain stuck for a long time, sometimes even for the rest of their life!

When Thomas was ten he could not, to save his life, understand science, and some unkind children called him 'dumbo'. Tom is a grown man now, with no qualifications and no chances of getting a good job. All because of a label, which made him lose confidence in his ability to learn. He simply gave up on himself.

Mary was quite plump when she was young and other children called her 'fatty'. She never said much, but it used to upset her a lot. Now she is sixteen and no longer fat but she still believes that she **is** fat because of the horrible label which she cannot forget. We can only hope she does not start slimming down. That could seriously harm her!

smile at yourself!

More about the wretched labels

You would be surprised to know how many people there are who have experienced the sad consequences of labels.

Where do labels come from?

Sometimes we want to hurt somebody, usually when we feel angry, helpless and don't know what else to do. Very often, though, labels are supposed to be jokes to make people laugh.

Beware: A joke which hurts other people is not a good joke!

You, like all of us, are capable of being

loving	or	cruel	respectful	or	hurtful
nasty	or	caring	bossy	or	co-operative
gentle	or	rough	polite	or	rude
silly	or	sensible	dishonest	or	truthful

AND IT'S THE SAME **YOU** BEHAVING IN ALL THOSE DIFFERENT WAYS!

smile at yourself!

We label people because we forget to distinguish between a person and what they do. In other words, instead of labelling the behaviour, we label the person. Next time someone does something wrong, instead of giving him or her a label, criticise their action.

For example,   instead of saying: say:

You stupid idiot!   *That was a stupid thing to do!*

You thief, you've taken my pen!   *I hate it when people take my things! Leave my pen alone!*

Can you see the difference? In describing and labelling actions you can still show your anger but you are not labelling a person who is just as capable of good as well as bad behaviour.

BEWARE OF LABELS: THEY CAN HARM YOU FOR LIFE

smile at yourself!

Practise labelling actions (not people!)

Example:

Your brother has broken your favourite cup.

Say: *That was totally careless! I am mad at you!*

Don't say: *I hate you, you clumsy idiot!*

Remembering to label the action and not the person, write down what you are going to say when:

1. Your friend has accidentally (?) torn up your picture.

....

....

2. Your brother has taken your pocket money without asking and has bought some sweets for himself.

....

....

3. A classmate has been calling you names.

....

....

NO PUT-DOWN ZONE! NO LABELLING!

Some of us become so used to labelling others that after a while we simply cannot do without it! Have you noticed that you don't like people who stick labels on you and avoid their company? That is because **negative labels are put-downs**. Who needs put-downs?! You can, if you choose to do so, learn to delete negative labels from your language.

Try these exercises. You may find them helpful.

CUT IT OUT!

Whenever you find yourself giving somebody a label, say to yourself quietly: *Cut it out!*

A few days later you will probably notice that it has become a little easier to stop yourself from putting others down.

Whether it is easier or not, continue to practise. You will improve with time.

NO PUT-DOWN ZONE

LABEL-FREE DAY AT HOME

Engage your whole family in the game: one whole day without any labels.

You may see that it is equally difficult for your mum as it is for you!

A day

TODAY

without Labels

Make a deal with your friend, sister or brother, that for one day neither of you will use any labels. Every time you manage to stop yourself from labelling a person congratulate yourself and give yourself a reward. Have your friend do the same thing.

Every time you forget about the deal and label someone, make a note on a sheet of paper.

At the end of the day count your successes and errors.

Do the exercise again.

YOU WILL MAKE PROGRESS!

smile at yourself !

Defence against labels

It is essential that you don't let any bad labels stick to you, ever!
Make sure you get rid of them before they pull you down, weaken
you, and take your confidence away.

LABEL-PROOF ARMOUR

Whenever someone tries to hurt you with nasty words or stick a label to you, put
on a magic suit of invisible, label-proof armour. It's incredible how well it works!

See in your mind's eye all the negative labels hit the armour and helplessly slide
down and fall to the ground without even touching you.

Remember that you always have the armour handy!

Just use it!

smile at yourself!

NO NEGATIVE LABELS FOR YOURSELF

Have you noticed that you do it to yourself? Isn't that strange that we set out to harm ourselves?

Cut out from your language phrases such as:
I am stupid! I never do anything right!
I am ugly and fat!
I am bad, useless and nobody loves me!

Every time you say something like that, quickly say to yourself: *cut it out!*

TEAR NEGATIVE LABELS OFF

Take a few self-sticking office labels and write on them hurtful words that other people have called you. Stick them to your clothes, look at yourself in the mirror, and feel how awful they are. Then tear them off slowly, one by one, saying: *I am throwing you away for ever!*

Tear the labels into small pieces and throw them in the bin.

You will need to do this exercise a few times if the labels have already stuck to you and it's not easy to get rid of them. But **you can do it!**

smile at yourself!

Protect your feeling of self-worth

No matter what others think or say about you, remember that you are absolutely unique, special and priceless. There is nobody like you in the whole world!

CAPTURE ALL PRAISING AND UPLIFTING WORDS

What is the nicest thing you have recently heard about yourself?

....

....

Anything else?

....

Who has last praised you and what exactly did they say?

....

Keep the list going and always have it handy in your *MAGIC BOX*.

smile at yourself!

Keep protecting your feeling of self-worth

Write down what you are good at and keep reminding yourself about it.

....

....

....

....

....

Surround yourself with people who believe in you. Is there anybody like that already?

....

....

....

Avoid comparing yourself with others.

Other people are certainly different.
Choose to see them as different,
not better or worse!

IF SOMEBODY IS PUTTING YOU DOWN, IT IS MORE THAN LIKELY
THAT THEY HAVE TROUBLE LIKING THEMSELVES

smile at yourself!

Your picture of yourself

Your self-image is the picture of **you**, which you carry in your heart and your head.
It affects how you feel, what you do, and how you do it.

People who see themselves in bright light or vibrant colours can get over difficulties and obstacles with a good dose of self-trust and confidence. They learn from their experiences and carry on doing whatever they were doing, with smiling faces.

Those whose self-portraits are dark and dim see themselves as if they were looking into a distorting mirror. Their reflections are ugly, completely mis-shapen and hardly resemble the real person. To those people their distorted images seem to be reflecting reality!

It is hard to live with a self-image like that. It disheartens us and drags us down.

smile at yourself!

Where do such distorted images come from?

Maybe somebody stuck a label to you and it is still there? They told you something and you didn't think they could be wrong?

....

Maybe you compared yourself with someone and decided you were not as good as they were?

....

Maybe you persistently told yourself that you **could not** do certain things and have programmed yourself for failure?

....

LABELS CAN BE PEELED OFF

COMPARING YOURSELF TO OTHERS MAKES LITTLE SENSE

IF YOU ARE CAPABLE OF PROGRAMMING YOUR BRAIN IN ONE WAY, YOU CERTAINLY CAN RE-PROGRAMME IT

smile at yourself!

Looking in the mirror

Stand in front of a mirror, look at yourself for a moment and ask yourself: *Do I like the person I am looking at?*

If your answer is 'yes', that's wonderful and you don't need to bother with the exercises to come. If, however, the person you are looking at is in your opinion not likeable, not very pretty, not very bright or not as good as others, we recommend that you do the exercises and not just once but every day for at least three weeks! Yes, we do believe it's **that** important!

Look again at your reflection in the mirror and wink to yourself. Make a few funny faces, smile charmingly and say something really nice to the person you are looking at:

I like you.

What a handsome young man you are!

I like your smile.

I am happy to be me.

Say it loud and clear at least three times and mean what you say!

Look at yourself and see a kind, capable and happy person. How, in your opinion, does a kind, happy and capable person look? What could you say about this person's actions, successes, plans? Has this person got friends? What kind of friends are they?

Write what you could expect from the happy and capable person you see in the mirror.

....

....

YOUR PICTURE OF YOURSELF WILL BE IN THE COLOURS OF YOUR CHOICE

smile at yourself!

What do you see in the mirror?

The picture of yourself, which you carry in your heart and your head, will influence the way you feel, your successes and your actions. You probably don't even know what power you have to decide what kind of person you see, how you behave and what you do.

And just think: the person you see in the mirror is always **you!**

Complete the sentences below:

When I see myself as a clever, reasonable person,

I ....

When I see myself as somebody stupid,

I ....

When I see an ugly creature in the mirror,

I ....

When I believe I am attractive,

I ....

When I see myself as a kind person,

I ....

When I see myself as a spiteful person,

I ....

IF YOU WANT, YOU CAN COMPLETELY AND EFFECTIVELY RE-PAINT YOUR PICTURE OF YOURSELF.

It's entirely up to you.

smile at yourself!

How to change your self-image

What you think about yourself is more important than what others think about you.
If your self-image is not good you will probably not believe in compliments people pay you
or nice things they say about you.

What to do to see yourself in a better light? We have already given you a few
ideas, but here are more tips that you can try out.

ACTING 'AS IF'

Behave as if you already were the kind of person you want to be.
For instance, if you are shy, start acting as if you were outgoing and
full of self-confidence.

Start by practising in front of a mirror. You will be surprised how
well you can imitate and then learn the behaviour you have always
admired in others.

smile at yourself!

PUT IT ON PAPER

Get yourself a special little notebook. Always keep it in the same place, so that you can easily find it any time you need it. Every time you have a success, even a very small one, write it down in your notebook. For example:

I cleaned up my room

I got very angry but I stopped myself from using labels

Even though I was scared, I admitted to having broken Mum's vase

I did my homework, even though there was an interesting film on TV

A SUCCESS BOARD

Ask your parents to buy you a notice board. You can get them quite cheap. Maybe you can use your pocket money to get one. Hang it on the wall in your room in a place where everybody, including you, can easily see it. Pin to the board everything that can remind you of your successes: photographs, diplomas, reports, letters, anything you are proud of.

MANY SUCCESSFUL PEOPLE USED THESE TIPS BEFORE THEY ACHIEVED THEIR DREAMS

smile at yourself!

My teacher Mr. Mistake

Have you ever met anybody who doesn't make mistakes? Of course not!

In spite of the fact that everybody makes mistakes, many people are afraid of making them. It makes them feel embarrassed and angry because they are afraid someone will think they are stupid or will laugh at them.

Being nasty to yourself because you have made a mistake is pointless and harmful to you. However, laughing at other people's mistakes is a truly horrible habit.

Mistakes are your teachers but only if you make good use of them. Some clever people know about it. Every time they make a mistake, they say:

A mistake?! Oops, no big deal. Let me correct it.

Memorise this and say it aloud or just silently to yourself whenever you make a mistake.

Say it also to other people if they go wrong. They will be grateful to you for not embarrassing them. Nobody enjoys embarrassment.

More about dealing with mistakes

Maybe, like many people, you get quite nervous about your mistakes and really upset when somebody points them out to you. Maybe making mistakes embarrasses you or makes you very angry. If this is so, try the exercises below.

Every time you make a mistake when doing your homework, wink at it and say:

Giggle, giggle. Just you wait, I'll get you!

Try to get some kind of electronic toy which makes funny noises. Whenever you make a mistake, press it and it will make you laugh. This way you will get used to treating your mistakes less seriously!

SQUEAK!

SQUEAK!

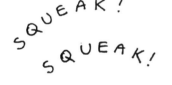

Play the 'strict teacher' game with a friend, your brother or sister. When you play the role of the teacher, criticise severely all the mistakes; when you play the pupil's role, calmly, without embarrassment say:

Oh, yes, that's right. I'll correct it straight away.

Whatever you do, don't let mistakes pull you down. They are here to teach you, not to embarrass or upset you.

THE MORE RELAXED YOU ARE, THE FEWER MISTAKES YOU MAKE

smile at yourself!

Believe in yourself!

It's not easy to think well of yourself if your schoolwork is not up to scratch. You see other children getting good grades and being praised by teachers, and your poor results worry you a lot although you may pretend you're not bothered. Whether your grades are good or not, always remember that **you are capable of doing better work**. Those children who lose trust in their ability have great trouble doing better work and getting higher grades.

I wonder whether you realise how much depends on your belief that YOU CAN DO IT! It is hard to imagine what difference believing in yourself can make.

Do any of the following apply to you?

- you have a problem at home which worries you a lot

- the way in which you are taught does not seem very good for you

- you are not very interested in what you are learning

- you don't seem to be able to concentrate on your work

Have you ever thought why your grades are not so wonderful? Think about some reasons and write them down.

....

....

....

SCHOOL REPORT

Albert Einstein
class 5B
GERMAN .... E
MATHS .... F
PHYSICS ...... F
this child will
never amount to anything

DOING EXERCISES IN THIS BOOK WILL HELP YOU SOLVE SOME OF YOUR PROBLEMS

Promises, promises

Keeping promises greatly improves the way we feel about ourselves. Not keeping promises does the opposite! It is better to avoid setting impossible goals and making promises you cannot keep. Learn to set manageable goals for yourself so that you can frequently praise yourself for achieving them.

Start to practise setting goals you can achieve quickly and easily. For example:

Every day for one week I will do three exercises from this book.

For the next four days I'll be kind to somebody I don't particularly like.

For two weeks I won't spend my pocket money.

Write down the goal that you want to achieve:

....

Now write it on a big sheet of paper and put it on your notice board. Every night give yourself a tick if you kept your promise. On the last day congratulate yourself and tell somebody, who understands the work you are doing, about your success.

WHEN I KEEP MY PROMISES, I RESPECT MYSELF

smile at yourself !

The art of wise self-confidence

When you disagree with somebody it is easy to get angry and say words you may regret later. Saying openly what you think and feel without hurting others is also a different kind of challenge. It may even be dangerous, especially if the other person is bigger, stronger or an adult with power over you. You may risk verbal or physical abuse from a stronger child or disapproval and punishment from an adult. There is no guarantee they will be less angry with you but there is a better chance you'll be able to communicate with them. That's why it's worth trying!

When you disagree with somebody, you have a choice:

a. You could shout, yell, call the person names, even hit them

b. You could say nothing, pretending nothing has happened (while you may be feeling disappointed or even furious with yourself)

c. You could firmly but politely express your thoughts and feelings, doing your best to hurt them as little as possible

WHEN YOU LEARN TO EXPRESS YOUR THOUGHTS AND FEELINGS WITHOUT HURTING THE OTHER PERSON, YOUR SELF-ESTEEM WILL SOAR TO THE SKY

Practise wise self-confidence

Now imagine what you will feel and think when someone disagrees with you and reacts in one of the following ways. Write your thoughts here:

in an aggressive way (see point a.) ....

....

in a passive way (see point b.) ....

....

in a reasonable, confident but polite way (see point c.) ....

....

smile at yourself !

Imagine the situations described below and write down:

- how you feel when someone is behaving in such a way

- what you think (if you can think at all at that moment)

- how you could respond with confidence and showing consideration for the other person's feelings

Your brother has eaten your dessert

A friend has come to visit you and started watching a video you don't want to watch

....

....

....

....

....

....

....

....

....

....

Your Mum is telling you off for being horrible to your younger sister

....

....

....

You are standing in a queue when suddenly an older boy pushes ahead of you

....

....

....

A child at school is laughing at you because your parents insist on knowing where you are and what you are doing at all times

....

....

EVERY TIME YOU REACT WITH CONFIDENT POLITENESS AND EXPRESS YOUR THOUGHTS AND FEELINGS, YOUR SELF-ESTEEM GETS HIGHER AND HIGHER

smile at yourself!

Go back to your responses. Are they clear and firm?
Would they hurt the other person?

If so, cross them out and in their place write better ones.

Now take a mascot or some cuddly toy and put it in front of you. Imagine your mascot is the person you have to tell how you feel and what you think. Talk to it as if it were a human being, using the responses you have written.

you're not supposed to call me names!

IT IS POSSIBLE TO TELL SOMEONE WHAT YOU THINK AND HOW YOU FEEL WITHOUT HURTING THEM AND FALLING OUT WITH THEM

smile at yourself !

Competitions

All contests and competitions may be great fun but they always carry with them one big risk: the risk of losing. Nobody likes to lose, but the trouble is there is usually only one winner and many 'losers'.

When you lose you have a choice:

- you can get angry, treat it as if it was the end of the world, lose your motivation and self-confidence
- you can treat it as a temporary setback, say to yourself that you'll do better next time, and this way protect your confidence and self-esteem

Every setback can teach you a lesson. You can figure out why you lost and what to do to have better chances next time:

Maybe you practised less than others did;

Maybe your concentration failed you;

Maybe you were not in top form;

Maybe somebody had better luck than you did.

A very good result is never as good as a better result. A result can always be improved.

That is why we recommend you delete the word 'failure' and replace it by 'result'.

The most important competition is the competition with yourself. Every time your result is better than before, you win.

IF DESPITE A LOWER RESULT YOU REMAIN YOUR OWN BEST FRIEND AND KEEP YOUR SELF-CONFIDENCE INTACT, YOU ARE A DOUBLE WINNER!

smile at yourself!

Criticism

There will always be someone who won't like what you do. Don't even try to please everybody to ensure that everybody likes you. If you do, you most probably won't like yourself because you won't know who you are.

Nobody likes to be criticised and nobody ever will. Critical remarks often cause a mixture of emotions: they make us feel angry and embarrassed, useless, inferior, wanting to fight or just disappear.

Learning to deal with criticism constructively takes a whole lifetime! It's a great challenge, so the earlier you start practising, the better! It is not so important whether the criticism is right or wrong. It is important to know how to learn from it, once the initial hurt and anger are over. When you learn that, you'll be a happier person.

YOUR WORTH AS A HUMAN BEING REMAINS INTACT
WHETHER SOMEONE CRITICISES YOU OR NOT

Dealing with criticism

ACCEPTING CRITICISM

Sit comfortably opposite a friend, your brother or sister, and ask them to tell you what they most like about you, and then what they don't like in your behaviour. Listen to your friend, remain silent for the whole time and say 'thank you' at the end. Now change places and tell your friend what you like about him or her and what you don't like about his or her behaviour. Do this exercise with a few people you like and who like you. This will teach you that you can hear out someone's critical remarks and still be friends!

NOT ACCEPTING CRITICISM

There are days when the last thing you want is to hear somebody criticising you. It just hurts too much and feels unbearable. For days like that, use your *INVISIBLE MAGIC ARMOUR*, the same one you have used to protect yourself from labels. When you call it in your imagination, it will appear immediately, covering you from head to toe. From this safe place you can watch the arrows of criticism breaking against the hard surface of your armour and falling helplessly to the ground.

WHEN YOUR SELF-ESTEEM IS IN GOOD SHAPE,
NO CRITICISM CAN DESTROY IT

smile at yourself !

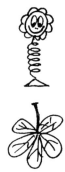

Sum it all up

Browse through all the exercises your have done in this section. Surely you must have liked some of them more than others!

Choose five exercises you like best and write down their titles:

1. ....

2. ....

3. ....

4. ....

5. ....

Write on a large sheet of paper how you will take care of your self-esteem. Use coloured markers and capital letters and draw colourful pictures to make it look pretty.

Take some BLU-TACK and stick the sheet to the wall in your room. Read your points every day until you know them by heart, until they become a part of you.

loosen up!

Smiling instantly lowers your stress

SMILE,

even when you don't really feel like smiling; **especially when you don't feel like it!**

Feel the smile relaxing your body, making it warmer, lighter...

Think for a moment:

What makes you laugh?

....

....

....

And what makes you smile?

....

....

perhaps a playful puppy, meeting a good friend, a sunny morning, the very thought of something yummy, seeing somebody else's smile...

loosen up!

Some things to make you smile

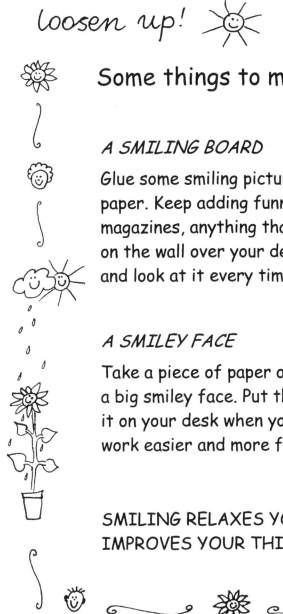

A SMILING BOARD

Glue some smiling pictures onto a large piece of thick paper. Keep adding funny pictures and jokes cut out of magazines, anything that makes you smile. Mount the paper on the wall over your desk where you do your homework and look at it every time you feel you need to relax.

A SMILEY FACE

Take a piece of paper of your favourite colour and draw on it a big smiley face. Put the drawing in a plastic sleeve and keep it on your desk when you work. You will probably find your work easier and more fun.

A BOOKMARK

Take smiling photographs of yourself, of you hugging your mum, your best friend, or cuddling your pet, and stick the photographs onto a narrow piece of cardboard. Attach to it some colourful pieces of thread and use it as your bookmark.

SMILING RELAXES YOUR MUSCLES AND YOUR BRAIN, IMPROVES YOUR THINKING AND YOUR ABILITY TO REMEMBER

loosen up!

Relaxation during your school lessons. Is that possible?

Sometimes you probably feel that the lessons will never end; your chair seems less and less comfortable as if it was growing spikes! Your legs move around nervously while your hands fidget with anything they can find.

Teachers don't like it when you behave that way. You would also like to remain calm and pay attention, if only you knew how to do it. Here are a few hints on how to relax without disturbing anybody.

breathe deeply in and out

TENSING AND RELAXING YOUR MUSCLES

Breathe... in... and out...

Sit up straight feeling your feet firmly on the floor. Push your toes into the floor, as if you wanted to make a hole in it. Count to five... and slowly let go. Then push you heels into the floor, count to five... and let go. Have you noticed how relaxed your feet have become?

Now put your hands on the knees, straighten your fingers and press, as if you wanted to press a rubber ball into the ground. Slowly release the pressure and relax your hands... See how calm they are now.

Sit up straight once more and feel your back firmly against the back of the chair. Press your back hard against the back of the chair, harder... harder... and slowly let go.

Notice how relaxed your body is now. Keep breathing... in... out... in... out...

loosen up!

More ways to relax during lessons

Whenever you feel nervous because you seem unable to solve a problem,
because you don't understand the lesson, or for any other reason:

take a deep breath and slowly breathe all the air out of your lungs...

As you breathe out, tilt your head down...

and let your shoulders and your jaw drop...

Bringing your head up, breathe in and press your tongue against the palate.

count to five... and breathe out...

Breathe in... and out... If nobody is looking, discreetly yawn...

Practise those exercises at home so that you can use them
any time you need to relax.

loosen up!

Everyday relaxation

To be relaxed does not mean to have no energy and feel like doing nothing. Not at all! Relaxation often gives you a lot of energy and an eagerness to do something, whatever this 'something' may be. Here are a few tips on how you can relax, feel lighter and full of energy.

THE NECK RUB

Place your hand on the back of your neck and squeeze...

Squeeze... and let go... squeeze... and let go... and again squeeze... and let go.

Tilt your head down and breathe out... Slowly lift your head... and breathe...

SHOULDER MASSAGE

Stand behind a friend and place your hands on her/his shoulders.

Now massage her/his shoulders and her/his neck.

Breathe... breathe... Now switch places and let her/him massage you.

A YAWN

Move your jaws a few times and with the fingers of both hands find the place where the jaw is attached to the skull. Making small circles with your fingertips massage the spots. Then stretch your arms and yaaaawn...

The amazing breath

Have you ever thought about the number of times you breathe in one minute, one hour, a day, during your whole life?

Take a watch which has a second-hand and count your breaths for one minute. Then, if you feel like it, you can take a calculator and establish the approximate number of breaths a person takes every year. Does the number surprise you?

breathe in

breathe in

Breathing = life. Everybody breathes but many people don't do a very good job of it. Their breath is shallow and does not give their bodies enough oxygen. We all need to learn to breathe well because a lot depends on the way we breathe:

> our health,
>
> our ability to relax,
>
> our ability to learn effectively.

When you start watching your breath it changes a little.

Observe your breath and see whether it becomes   faster or slower?

deeper or more shallow?

Practising your amazing breath

Sit on a chair or on something soft on the floor.

Sit up straight but make sure you feel comfortable.

Close your eyes...

Massage your jaw and let it drop...

Shake your shoulders, feel them drop too...

Now let your arms hang loose...

Feel your hands become a little tingly, then warmer... and warmer...

Breathe... once again breathe... and again...

Keep breathing rhythmically or freely, deeply or normally, whichever feels right.

freely... rhythmically... slowly... deeply... in... out

Stretch like a cat that has just woken up, and slowly open your eyes.

loosen up!

In the Land of Peace and Calm

Turn on some slow, calming music... (try music on your companion CD)

Lie down on a soft blanket or a carpet...

Close your eyes... breathe in... and out... in... out... in... out...

Listen to the music... breathe the music in... and out...

Lift one leg off the floor... and let it drop. Now the other one... let it drop...

Lift one arm... and let it drop... The other arm... and let go...

Breathing calmly, feel any tension in your body. Take a breath and, breathing out, send the warm, relaxing energy to that place...

Feel the tense muscles relax...

Any more tension? Breathe in again, and when breathing out send the relaxing, warm energy to the tense spot in your body...

When the whole of your body feels warm and relaxed,

breathe in deeply and let all the air out of your lungs...

Stretch... stretch... your legs... arms...

Turn to your side slowly, open your eyes

and sit up feeling relaxed, happy and full of energy.

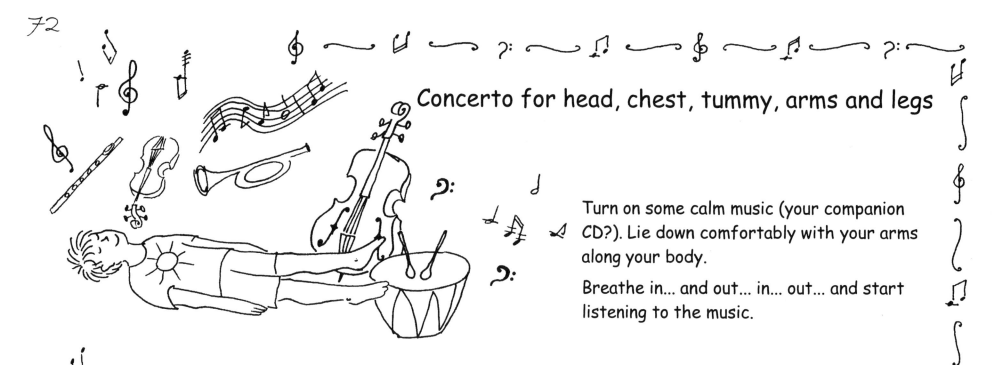

Concerto for head, chest, tummy, arms and legs

Turn on some calm music (your companion CD?). Lie down comfortably with your arms along your body.

Breathe in... and out... in... out... and start listening to the music.

Imagine that the sounds you hear are coming out of the different parts of your body, as if your body was playing the music... The lower sounds are being played by your legs and the tummy while the higher notes are coming out of your chest, arms and your head.

Keep listening to the music, 'playing' the music with your body... Breathe... breathe...

Feel how relaxing and pleasant it is...

loosen up!

Exercise and relax your eyes

Working or playing with computers, watching television as well as reading for a considerable period of time (particularly if the lighting is bad!) make your eyes very tired. As they hardly move, they don't get enough exercise and become sore and tense.

Close your eyes and put your head gently as far back as it will go without your neck hurting.

Keeping your eyes closed, 'look' at your forehead... now at your chin... to the left... and to the right...

Now slowly roll your eyes clockwise... and anti-clockwise...

Cover your eyes with both hands
and slowly open them.

smile

loosen up!

Relax and 're-charge your batteries'

To be able to work well we need to be in a state of relaxed alertness. Sometimes relaxation is not enough; we may still feel too lazy to get down to work. If you feel that way too, try the exercises which, while relaxing your body, will also give you extra energy and help you 're-charge your batteries'.

BREATHING THROUGH YOUR FEET

Lie down on the carpet. Straighten your arms and put them behind your head, the back of your palms touching the floor. Hold your breath. Tighten your arms and legs, pressing them into the floor. Count to three... Breathing out, lift your hands and put them along your body. Breathe a few times... in... out... in... out...

Now imagine you are breathing with your feet.

When you breathe in, the air comes through the feet, and goes further through the legs, back, neck, up to the top of your head. When you breathe out, the air goes back the same way and leaves through your feet.

Breathe in - from the feet to the top of your head.

Breathe out - from the top of your head to your feet.

With every breath, feel your body fill up with energy...

Just a few minutes of this kind of breathing will be enough to make you want to do some work.

breathe in

breathe in

and out

and out

loosen up!

Relaxed alertness

You can do this exercise while sitting in a chair, so it may be useful during your lessons at school.

breathe deeply in and out

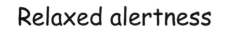

YOUR BREATHING BODY

Start with your legs: imagine that the air comes into your body, first through your feet and calves, then through your thighs. Breathe three times through your legs. Feel the air come in and go out through your legs...

Now breathe with your tummy...

your chest...

your neck...

your head...

With every breath, feel your energy level rise and your mind become clearer and more alert.

loosen up!

The cat's stretch

Animals are amazingly good at relaxing... you can learn a great deal from them, observing and imitating them. When you start getting tired of doing your homework and find yourself absent-mindedly staring at the wall, take a short break and lie on the carpet.

Can you remember what a cat who has just woken up looks like?

The front paws stretched as far as they can reach...

Then the body arched, the neck stretched... the head up...

All the muscles tensed and then relaxed... tensed and relaxed...

Become a cat... move like a cat.

You can also make some cat noises.

When you feel relaxed and alert go back to your homework.

Relax even when you are angry

Controlling your emotions is a skill, difficult but extremely useful.

Can you remember your last quarrel with a friend or a relative?

What was it about? ....

What did you tell them? ....

What did they say? ....

How did you feel after the fight? ....

What did you think? ....

Now imagine you are this very person you quarrelled with.

Can you imagine how they felt after the fight? ....

and what they thought? ....

How could you two have avoided the quarrel? ....

An argument with a friend usually ends well. However, rude and uncontrolled behaviour may have very unpleasant consequences!

loosen up!

Relax even when you are angry

Anger is a very powerful emotion.

If you are like most of us, you too sometimes feel hurt, angry, maybe even furious! Then all you can think of is hitting the people who made you angry and calling them the worst names under the sun. You may even do that!

If only you could stop for a second and listen to what your mind and heart say...

So why does anger manage to take over?

Because when we get angry, thinking is extremely difficult, even impossible.

When you are angry ask your heart

Next time somebody makes you really angry and you feel that all you want to do is beat him up and call him rude names, say to yourself:

STOP, FREEZE AND BREATHE!

Stand motionless and silent...

Breathe in... and out... in... and out...

Imagine you are breathing through your heart...

Put your hand on your heart...

Feel your anger and bad thoughts melt away in the warmth

of your heart...

Keep breathing... slower... slower... deeper... deeper...

in... out... in... out... in... out...

Ask your heart what to do next and listen carefully to what it says.

Now you can think clearly and you will know what to do.

loosen up!

Let your anger melt away

When you feel annoyed and angry with someone, quickly leave the room and go somewhere where you can be alone and undisturbed.

Stand straight and breathe...

Cross one ankle over the other.

Stretch your arms in front of you, back of hands together, thumbs pointing down.

Still keeping your arms stretched out, thumbs down, cross right hand over left, so palms are facing.

Interlock fingers and thumbs.

Turn wrists inwards till you reach position in the picture.

Stay in that position counting your breaths until your anger melts away.

Go back to the room and tell the person how you feel and what has made you angry.

loosen up!

Your favourite things

We feel good, calm and fully relaxed when we are with the people we love, and when we are surrounded with our favourite things.

Think for a moment and write in the lines below:

your favourite flower .... your favourite place ....

your favourite colour .... your favourite song ....

your favourite animal .... your favourite object ....

Now choose one of your favourite things, imagine it as clearly as you can, and then draw it, glue its photograph, or if it's a song, write its title in the frame.

Remember your favourite thing! It will make you smile and help you relax.

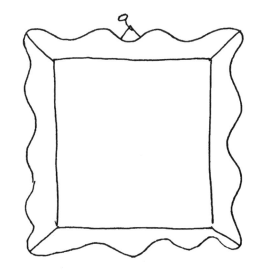

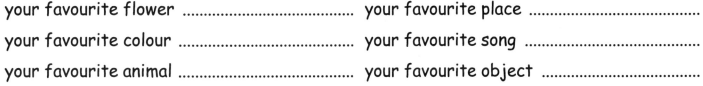

loosen up!

Do things HAVE TO stress you out?

Not at all!

People react in different ways to the same thing or situation:

   some may find it enjoyable, interesting or amusing;

   others may see it as hurtful, irritating, boring or scary.

   There may still be others who will find it not worth thinking about.

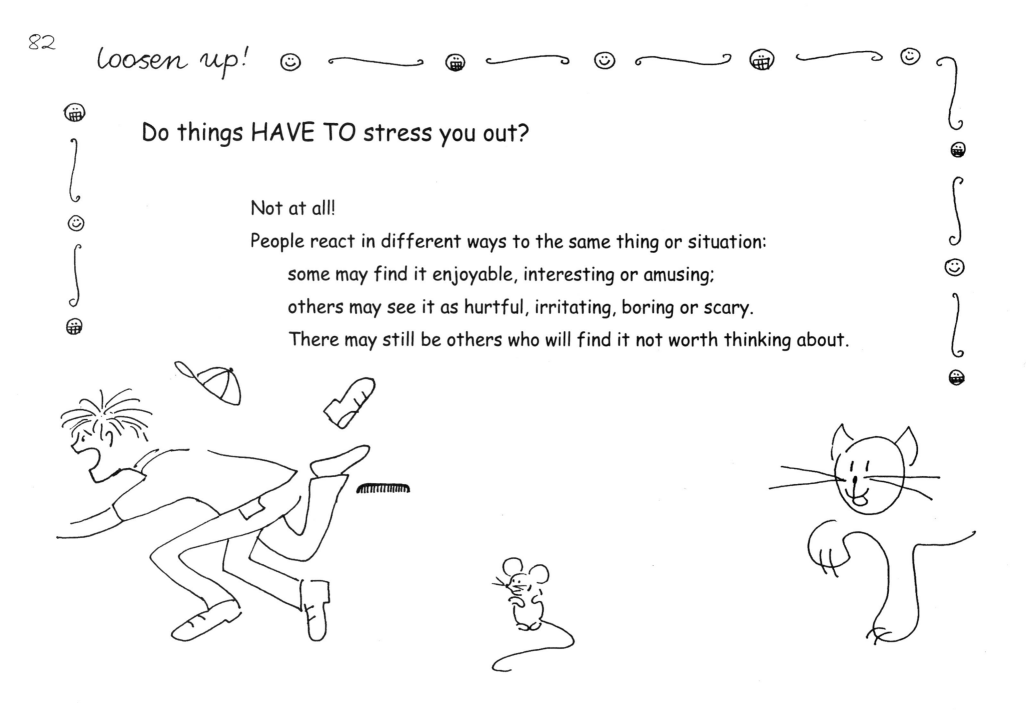

loosen up!

A great deal depends on the words you use when talking about people, things or events. If you constantly repeat phrases such as ' history is boring' or 'maths is terrible', there is hardly a chance you will ever like those subjects. However, if instead you try saying 'history may be interesting' or 'it is possible to understand maths', your attitude towards these subjects will change and the stress they cause you will disappear.

It is also true when you talk about people. You may keep saying that you don't like Mary and that she gets on your nerves, but remember, other people like her, so she can't be all bad.

If you just make an effort, you will notice her good points and no longer see Mary as irritating.

loosen up!

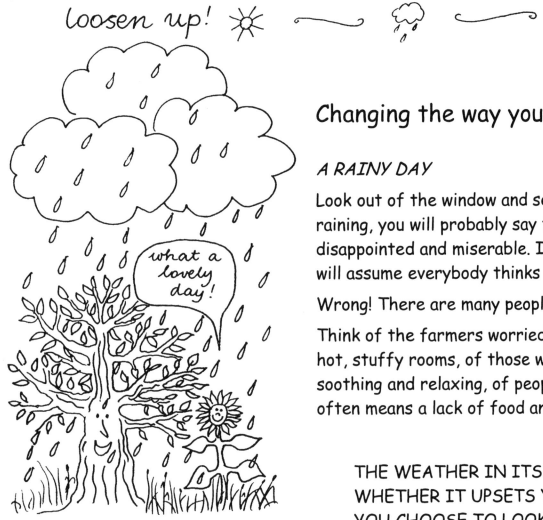

what a lovely day!

Changing the way you see things

A RAINY DAY

Look out of the window and see what the weather is like. If it's raining, you will probably say that the weather is horrible, and feel disappointed and miserable. If, however, you see the sun shining, you will assume everybody thinks that the day is beautiful.

Wrong! There are many people who prefer rain!

Think of the farmers worried about their crops, of people working in hot, stuffy rooms, of those who find the sound of the falling raindrops soothing and relaxing, of people in all the countries where drought often means a lack of food and drinking water.

THE WEATHER IN ITSELF IS NEITHER GOOD NOR BAD. WHETHER IT UPSETS YOU OR NOT DEPENDS ON THE WAY YOU CHOOSE TO LOOK AT IT.

loosen up!

Changing the way you see situations

How do you feel about flying?

> There are those who are scared stiff of aeroplanes,
> and those for whom flying is the greatest possible fun.

And public performances?

> Some people love taking part in school shows,
>
> while for others the very thought of appearing in public is terrifying.

If you want, you can change the way you look at certain situations and in this way reduce the stress they cause you.

**IT IS THE WAY WE CHOOSE TO LOOK AT THINGS THAT CAUSES STRESS,
NOT THE THINGS THEMSELVES**

loosen up!

The soothing power of music

It is impossible to imagine the world without music, although not all of us like the same kind of music.

Our mood can depend on the music we listen to, and the music we listen to greatly depends on our mood.

Find tapes with slow music, e.g. classical music by Bach, Handel, Vivaldi or Mozart (have you tried your companion CD?), and listen to it when you read, do your homework, or feel anxious and irritable.

It will have a soothing effect on your mood.

You will have noticed that not all music calms you down. Deep relaxation needs a specific kind of music.

Did you know that very loud noises, particularly from low-pitched instruments, such as the bass-guitar and percussion, could harm your concentration and memory? It may also permanently damage your hearing!

If you like disco music, listen to it after you have done your homework.

loosen up!

The soothing power of nature

Lie on the grass, in the shade of a big tree...

Look up...

See the branches, against the blue-grey background of the sky...

Thousands of leaves gently moving with the breeze...

Watch the clouds passing by...

observe their fantastic shapes, always changing...

Do they remind you of anything?

A sheep? A house?

Now listen... Hear the birds sing...

How many different sounds can you distinguish?

Can you hear any other sounds?...

The murmuring of water...

or the wind in the trees?

THE BEAUTY OF MUSIC AND NATURE
MAY GIVE YOU A SENSE OF UNITY
WITH THE UNIVERSE

loosen up!

Sum it all up

Leaf through the pages of this section. Can you point to your favourite exercises?

Choose five most useful for you and write them down:

1. ....

2. ....

3. ....

4. ....

5. ....

Take a large sheet of blank paper, put it on its side and write in the centre: LOOSEN UP.

Draw five branches coming out of the centre and on each branch write the name of your chosen exercise.

Draw a picture of the exercises next to the branches. Make them colourful and fun.

With a blob of BLU-TACK stick the sheet to the wall in your room.

Practise the exercises every day, when you get up and before you go to bed, until you master the art of relaxation.

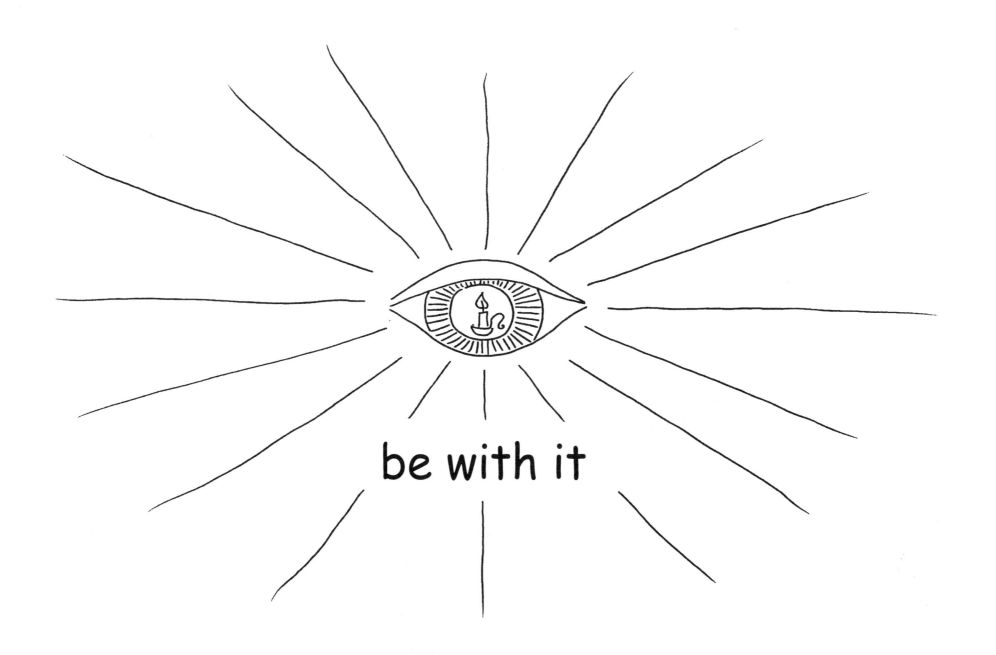

be with it

be with it

Focusing your senses

Remember looking at a blurred, out of focus photograph? All the shapes and colours seem to be clouded and misty... You can't even figure out exactly what the shapes or colours are.

When we are not concentrating and our attention wanders, our minds are very much like this photograph: out of focus, clouded, misty. We feel as if we were outside of ourselves viewing the world through an opaque glass, living in a world of our own, not connected to what is happening around us. It may be a lovely state to be in but not very helpful when you are learning something or trying to understand a lesson.

If you want to see things clearly, hear everything around you and be aware of what is going on, your senses need focusing like a telescope.

The exercises on the next few pages will help you do just that.

Get into your centre

Stand up with your feet firmly on the ground.

Feel your feet connect with the ground as if they were sinking into it.

Close your eyes, imagine your centre and put your hand on that spot.

Feel it become warm and relaxed...

Breathe in your favourite colour, and out... in... out...

Now imagine you are tiny, so tiny that you can hold yourself in one hand.

Put the tiny you in your centre. Feel good, warm and safe.

Still feeling the comfort and warmth, start growing...

Grow bigger... and bigger... and bigger... until you are the actual size of your body...

Stay with the good feeling and open your eyes, still keeping your hand on your centre of balance.

Then slowly let go...

be with it

The candle light

Ask an adult to be with you while you do this exercise.

Light a candle and place it safely in a candlestick or a bowl on a small coffee table. Draw the curtains and turn the light off.

Sit down on the floor on a comfortable cushion...

Breathe in... out... in... out... watching the flame.

Stay motionless... silent... just breathing and watching the flame...

Look at the flame... can you see any shapes?... different colours?...

Still watching the flame, imagine getting inside it, becoming one with it...

Stay with the feeling and breathe... breathe... until you are calm and focused.

Tick-tock of the clock

Take a big clock with a second hand off the wall

(make sure you ask your Mum first!)

Put the clock in front of you, and let it lean safely against the wall.

Now put your hand on your navel and breathe... breathe...

Breathing freely... in... out... in... out... look at the clock. What time is it?

Now look at the second hand on the clock and start watching it go round and round...

Once... twice... three times...

Keep on breathing and watching the second hand...

If you realise that your eyes have wandered away, gently bring them back.

Look at the clock. What time is it? How long have you been watching the second hand?

Next time, try to do it longer.

be with it

One breath... two breaths...

Sit comfortably on the floor or on a chair, whichever feels better.

Gently massage the places where your jaw is attached to your skull, let your jaw drop...

Shake your shoulders and your arms, and let them drop, too.

Close your eyes and breathe freely... breathe... breathe...

Start watching your breath... feel the cold air touch your nostrils when you breathe in...

and the warm air tickle your nose as you breathe out...

Now start counting your breaths,

    one... two... three... four... five...

How many breaths did you take before you stopped counting?

Write down the number ....

Next time when you count your breaths you may reach a higher number.
Write it down every time and watch your progress!

be with it

BRAIN BUTTONS

With the thumb and the middle finger, find two small dents below the collar bones and gently rub them.

Place the other hand on your navel and breathe... breathe...

Rubbing the *BRAIN BUTTONS* will immediately help you get focused.

Remember to massage your *BRAIN BUTTONS* every time you feel tired and find it difficult to think.

It works!

HELICOPTER SPIN

Stand in the middle of the room and spread your arms out from the sides of your body. Turn around slowly making sure you have enough space and that nothing is in your way. With your arms stretched out like a bird's wings, spin as if you were a propeller on top of a helicopter.

Spin only in one direction, preferably clockwise.

Start with only a few spins and when you feel more confident, you can spin 12-15 times. Take a break and do it again.

When you stop, put your hands together in front of you, as if you were about to pray; look at the tips of your fingers until the world stops going round and round...

Take a deep breath...

This exercise can greatly improve your learning ability and help you focus attention on whatever you want to do.

Walking with your eyes wide open and your ears well tuned

Ask a grown-up to take you to the park or to the woods. If there is nobody who can go with you, simply go to the garden.

Stand still for a moment and breathe...

Slowly walk around... Then say to yourself: *Listen... listen... listen...*

Stop and close your eyes. Keep still and silent... What sounds can you hear?...

After a while, open your eyes and write in your notebook what you have heard.

Start walking slowly, this time with your eyes open.

Look at the plants. How many varieties can you see? Can you name some of them?

Write in your notebook the names of the plants you can name and draw the ones whose names you don't know.

Have you noticed plants you have never seen before? If you develop a habit of paying attention to the world around you, you will have many wonderful and unexpected experiences. On top of that, learning will become much easier!

BUTTERFLY'S WINGS

Stand in the middle of the room where you can have plenty of space.

Breathe freely... in... out... in... out...

Keep your feet about 30cm apart and bend your knees.

Put your hands in front of you and interlock the fingers, with the thumbs forming a cross.

Start drawing the wings of a butterfly in the air:

begin in the middle where the lines cross,

go up to the right and down;

through the middle, up to the left and down;

up to the right down; up to the left, down, and so on.

Keep your eyes on the spot where the thumbs cross.

Now make a fist with your right hand and, keeping your eyes on the sticking out thumb, draw *BUTTERFLY'S WINGS* in the air.

Change hands and do the same with your left hand.

And now both hands together...

Your head stays in one place, only your eyes and arms move!

THE CRANE

Did you know that some movement exercises help focus attention and improve memory?

Here is one of them:

Place your left ear on your left shoulder and extend your left arm...

Now you look like a crane with a very long bill.

With the extended arm draw in the air a few small circles and then a few *BUTTERFLY'S WINGS.*

Keep looking at your finger tips drawing the *BUTTERFLY'S WINGS.*

Now do the same exercise with your right shoulder, ear, and arm.

BREATHE ALL THE TIME!

Shake your shoulders and your arms, and let them drop. BREATHE...

be with it

Your focus supporters

Holding something small in your hand can often help you concentrate on what you are doing.
There are people who simply can't concentrate without it!

Many children like holding different things such as conkers, smooth pebbles,
tiny figures, marbles, or soft, cuddly mascots.

Is there anything you like holding in your hand while reading, thinking,
learning something by heart or doing your homework?

What is it?...

One girl even made for herself a soft, velvet heart with a smiley face
on it, and carries it with her in her pocket at all times. Whenever she
feels a little nervous, upset or she can't concentrate, she puts her hand
in her pocket and feels the warmth of her velvet heart.
She says it certainly makes her feel better.

If you think you need a focus supporter, get one for yourself, keep it in your pocket,
and hold it in your hand whenever you need it. You may find it really helpful!

be with it

Listening with all your heart

Opening your heart will help you stay focused and understand what the other person is **really** trying to say. Cut out two hearts out of a piece of thick felt. Then cut out openings as shown in the picture. Put the hearts on your ears. This will remind you to listen with your heart when someone wants to talk with you, to **really** listen...

TEN MINUTE LISTENING EXERCISE

Make a deal with your friend that every day each of you will spend ten minutes telling the other one about the events of the previous day. Put your listening hearts on and listen to your friend with all your heart and attention. Then change places and tell your friend your story.

How does it feel to be really listened to?

....

....

be with it !

Fixing your attention on the page

On the next page there is a text I would like you to play with for a while.

Take green, yellow, blue, and pink markers and

* with the blue one circle all the question marks and exclamation marks

* with the pink one circle all the words starting with 'b'

* with the green one circle all the letters appearing in your first name

* with the yellow one circle the alphabet in proper order

Find another text in a magazine or a newspaper and this time choose four different markers. Decide on the order in which you will use the colours and circle as fast as you can:

* all the nouns

* all the verbs

* all the adjectives

* all the vowels: a, e, i, o, u

Time yourself and write how long it has taken you to complete the task ....

be with it

It is much easier to concentrate on something we find interesting, something we have chosen for ourselves, than to focus attention on a task somebody else tells us we 'should' or 'must' do. Usually we find the things we have to do pretty boring, tiring, and not easy to concentrate on. Remember, last week in class you felt sleepy and bored when suddenly the teacher gave you a sheet of paper with a problem to solve. Oh, dear! That wasn't fun! You just couldn't pull yourself together to do any work at all...

And a few days ago you were happily watching a film on television when you suddenly remembered the homework about Ancient Greece for the next day! You were so very tired, sleepy and angry with yourself that you had forgotten about your homework... How on earth were you going to have enough energy to concentrate on the job?

You didn't know then but you know now! In class you can gently massage your *BRAIN BUTTONS* which will immediately stimulate the brain. And at home you could do so many different things! *THE CRANE*, the *HELICOPTER SPIN*, the *BUTTERFLY'S WINGS*, and breathing exercises will always come to your rescue.

be with it

Sum it all up

Go back to the beginning of this section of the book and look through it once again.

Can you remember which of the exercises were specially good for you?

Choose five of the ones you like and write them down:

1. ....

2. ....

3. ....

4. ....

5. ....

If you haven't chosen the *HELICOPTER SPIN*, make it your sixth one. It is very important! Take a large sheet of blank paper and put it on its side. In the centre draw a picture which will symbolise 'focus' or 'attention'. Draw five branches coming out of the central picture and write on them your favourite focusing exercises. Draw as many pictures as you can to illustrate the exercises. Glue the sheet to the wall with BLU-TACK, so that you can see it every time you walk into your room.

Do the chosen exercises regularly, remembering to start the day with a *HELICOPTER SPIN*.

the way YOU learn best

the way YOU learn best

Discover the best way you learn

Did you know that everybody learns in his own, unique way? This is why not every way of learning is suitable for everybody. This is also why every child should be taught in a different way, but obviously this would not be possible to do at school.

In this section of the book, we have prepared for you a number of exercises which will help you discover your very best and unique way of learning. You will see how much easier and more pleasant learning will be when you know how to do it in full agreement with your needs.

Let's start with finding out why you learn.

the way YOU learn best

Why do we learn?

There is always a reason we learn things but we don't always bother to stop and think what it is. When we know **why**, we learn faster and better.

You have learned an incredible number of things in your life so far, and this exercise will help you find out why you've learned them.

On the next page you can see some bare branches. Write on them what exactly you have learned because:

> it was fun
>
> it was interesting
>
> somebody told you to
>
> you needed to know
>
> ? (you haven't got a clue!)

There are certain things we learn for more than just one reason.

Feel free to write the same thing twice, even three times.

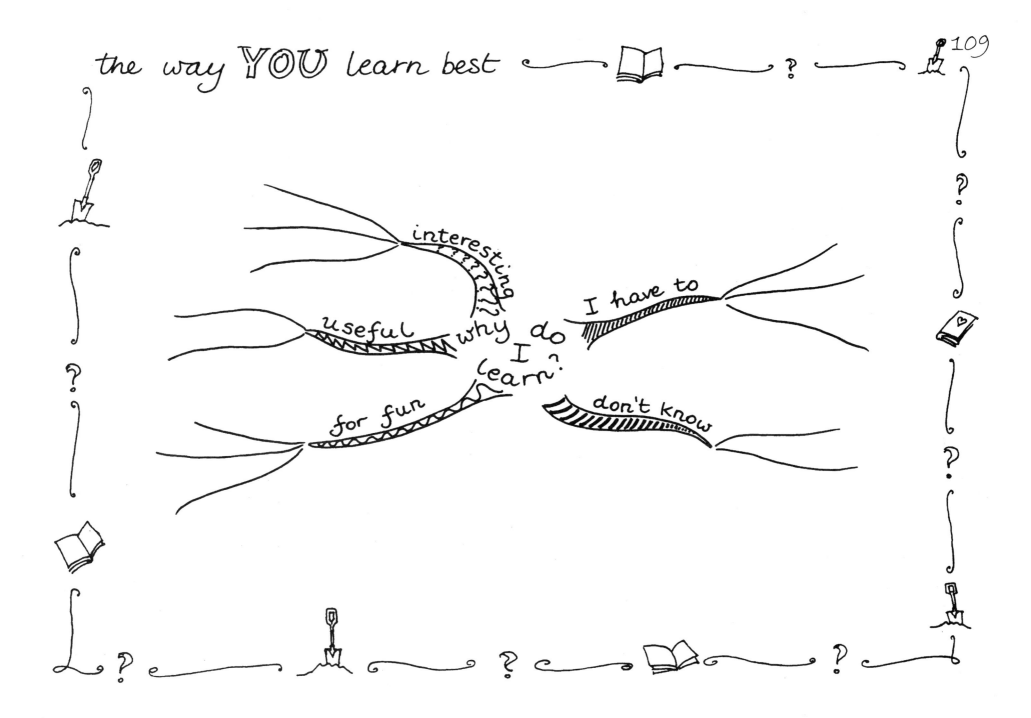

the way YOU learn best

interesting !?!?!

useful

why do I learn?

for fun

I have to

don't know

the way YOU learn best

You are born with a passion for learning!

This is absolutely true although you may sometimes wonder why you don't always feel that way.

Before your third birthday you had already learned an incredible number of skills and acquired an understanding of many very complicated processes.

the way YOU learn best

Write down five things you
have learned so far, with little
help from others or maybe
with no help at all:

How did you learn these things?
Did you imitate someone?
Did you have to practise a lot?
Who helped you and how?

....

....

....

....

....

....

....

....

the way YOU learn best

How did you learn these?

Mark how you've learned the skills listed below, ticking one or more columns.

Skill	from parents or teachers	from books or films	from friends	by myself	don't know
dancing					
walking					
coping with anger					
playing ball					
reading					
making phonecalls					
using times tables					
using a knife and fork					
riding a bike					
caring for pets					
ancient history					

the way YOU learn best

How will you learn these?

Mark how you would choose to learn the skills in this table, ticking one or more columns.

How will you learn?	breeding horses	driving a car	making cakes	a foreign language	to work a computer	about Nobel Prize winners
read a book						
watch a film						
go to museum, stables, factory						
use a computer						
ask a teacher						
do it myself						
get advice from a friend						

the way YOU learn best

Your most important sense

We find out about the world by listening, touching, smelling, tasting and looking. We use our senses and our intuition every time we learn something.

Some people are equally at home using all their senses but most of us use one or two senses more than others. In order to learn, some of us need to touch and do things, others prefer to hear when someone talks to them, and still others can't learn without seeing things.

This is why we call people:
visual
   (those who need to see),
auditory
   (those who need to hear),
or **kinesthetic**
   (those who need to move),
depending on their preferred sense.

Do you know whether you belong to one of these groups? It is important to know, because if you're trying to learn something by hearing while your dominant sense is your sight, you will be making learning more difficult for yourself.

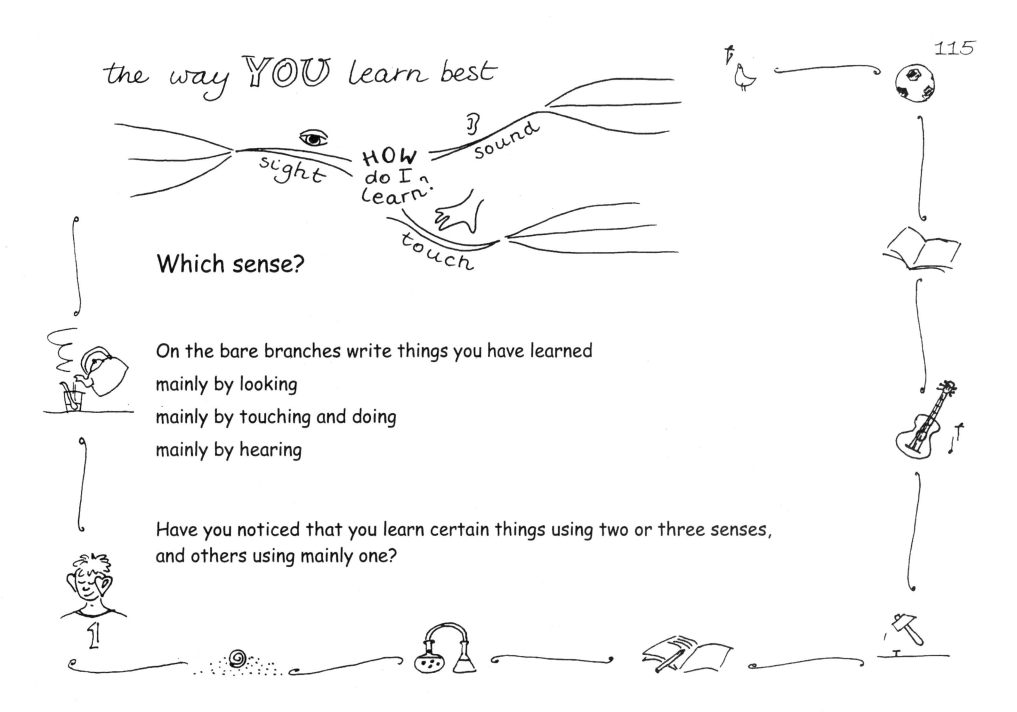

the way YOU learn best

sight

HOW do I learn?

sound

touch

Which sense?

On the bare branches write things you have learned

mainly by looking

mainly by touching and doing

mainly by hearing

Have you noticed that you learn certain things using two or three senses, and others using mainly one?

the way YOU learn best

Learning something by heart

Which of the following ways is your favourite?

1. You sit at the desk, read silently to yourself, close your eyes and repeat.

2. You like it when someone reads the lesson to you.

3. You enjoy nibbling while you learn.

4. You walk around the room with the book in your hand, repeating the text aloud; you may hold some small object in the other hand and from time to time pick a sweet or bite an apple.

If you recognise yourself in the first description, you are probably a visual learner.

Number two is an auditory learner.

For the third learner, the sense of taste seems to be important.

The fourth one is a learner, who in order to learn needs to move, touch and do.

YOUR FAVOURITE WAY TO LEARN MAY BE A MIXTURE OF TWO OR MORE WAYS

the way YOU learn best

And now imagine yourself at school and think when you learn best:

Is it when:

you look at the board, at pictures in the book, when you read, or watch a film?

you listen attentively to the teacher?

you make models or act out some situation?

REALISING WHAT WAY IS BEST FOR YOU

WILL HELP YOU HELP YOURSELF!

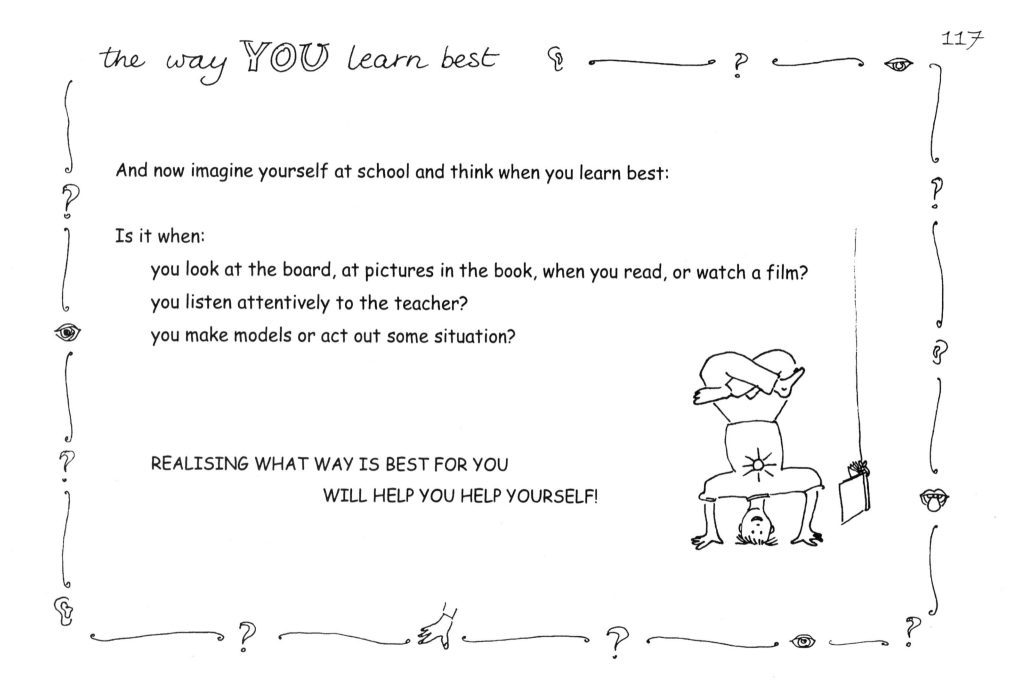

the way YOU learn best

Discover how you learn best

Take a pencil and (circle) your answers. You may have more than one for every question!

1. I prefer to read

   lying on my tummy
   sitting at the desk
   lying on the sofa or in bed

2. I prefer learning

   in the library

   in my room

   in the living room

   in the park or in the garden

3. While I do my homework I usually

   don't mind whether there is music or not

   listen to soft music

   like loud and rhythmic music

   need absolute silence

4. I learn best

   with a friend

   all by myself

   with a teacher or a parent

   in a group of people

5. When I learn something I like to

   walk around the room

   sit at my desk or at the table

   sit on a sofa or a bed

   sit or lie on the floor

6. When I have to learn something I prefer to

   read about it in a book

   watch a film on the subject

   have someone tell me about it

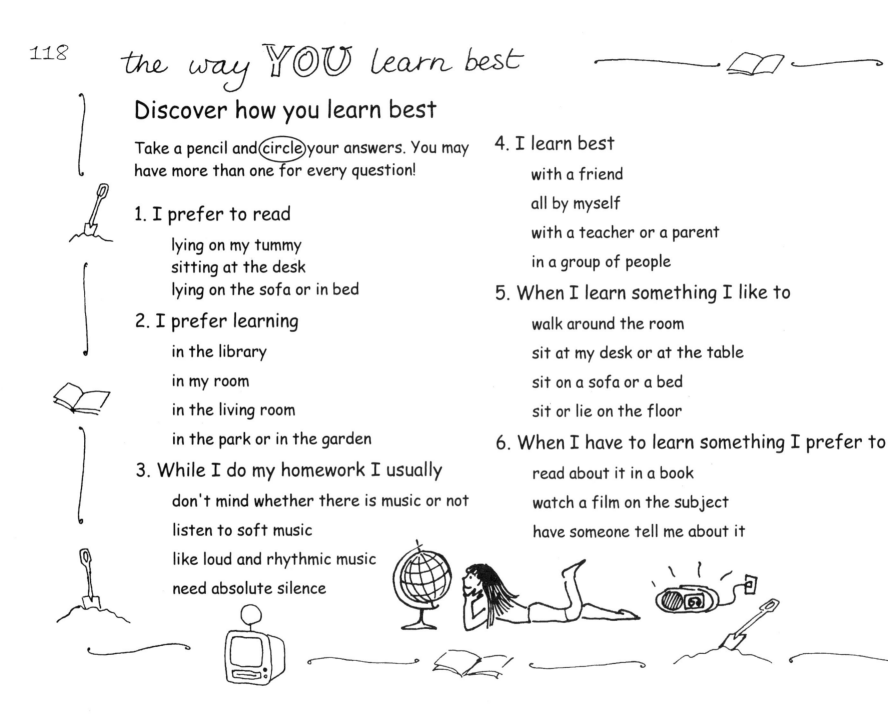

Now find your answers on this page.

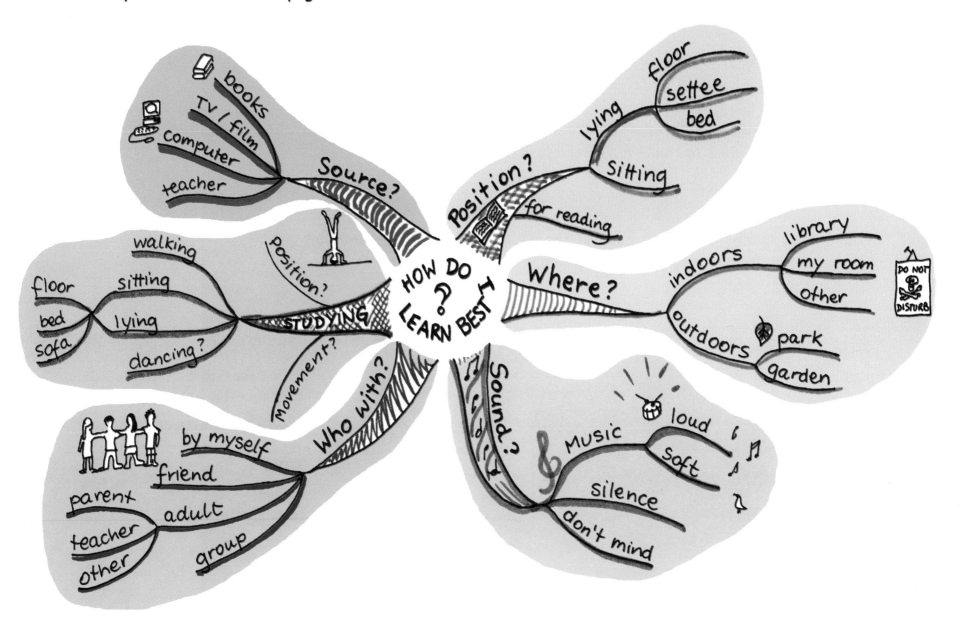

the way YOU learn best

Your incredibly amazing brain

Information comes to us through the senses of sight, hearing, touch, smell and taste. Then it goes to the brain where it is processed, understood and memorised.

The brain has two hemispheres. Each of them has its own tasks to perform and is special in its own way.

THE LEFT HEMISPHERE

takes care of words, numbers, lists, facts, details, graphs, analytical thinking.

It is responsible for conscious learning.

THE RIGHT HEMISPHERE

takes care of patterns, rhythm and sound, visual images, colour, and 'global picture' of things.

It is responsible for sub-conscious learning.

More about hemispheres

Everybody uses both hemispheres but most of us have one which is more active than the other. This is why we talk about left-brain or right-brain people.

Both hemispheres are equally important but most of the work you do at school requires the services of your left hemisphere. The right one is only too often neglected and ignored.

The exercises we have designed for you will help you see which of your hemispheres seems to be more active. They will also suggest what you need to do to activate the other one.

KNOWLEDGE ABOUT YOUR AMAZING BRAIN

WILL HELP YOU FIND THE BEST WAY TO USE IT

the way YOU learn best

The right or the left hemisphere?

Discover how your brain works. Put a tick where the answer is 'yes'.

In this exercise every answer is right; there are no wrong answers!

Do you like music? ☐ Dancing? ☐ Drawing pictures? ☐ Do you enjoy daydreaming? ☐

Is touching more important for you than seeing or hearing? ☐

Do you like very colourful things? ☐

In order to understand how an engine works do you have to see it in real life? ☐

Do you sympathise with others when you know they are in pain? ☐

Do you want to know how a book ends before you start reading it? ☐

Do you tend to leave things half-done? ☐

If you have ticked six or more little squares, most probably your right hemisphere is very active.

With the right brain really active you obviously have some wonderful abilities.

You may also need to work on activating the left hemisphere to make your school work more effective.

The right or the left hemisphere? - yet again

Put a tick where your answer is 'yes'.

Do you like joking about things? ☐

Do you sometimes find it awkward to find the right word to express what you feel or think? ☐

Does time pass without you being aware of it? ☐

Do you protest when asked to do something step by step? ☐

Are details not very important for you because you only need to see the whole picture? ☐

Are you a rebel trying to change things around you to meet your needs? ☐

Do you sometimes use words in the wrong sense ☐ or interpret them incorrectly? ☐

Are you often late ☐ ? Is it difficult for you to find time for the things you need to do? ☐

If you have ticked most of the squares, you most probably have a strong tendency to work with your right brain and you are a free, creative spirit! This is truly wonderful. You may, however, need to work on your left brain to be good at your school work, too. Try the exercises on the next few pages.

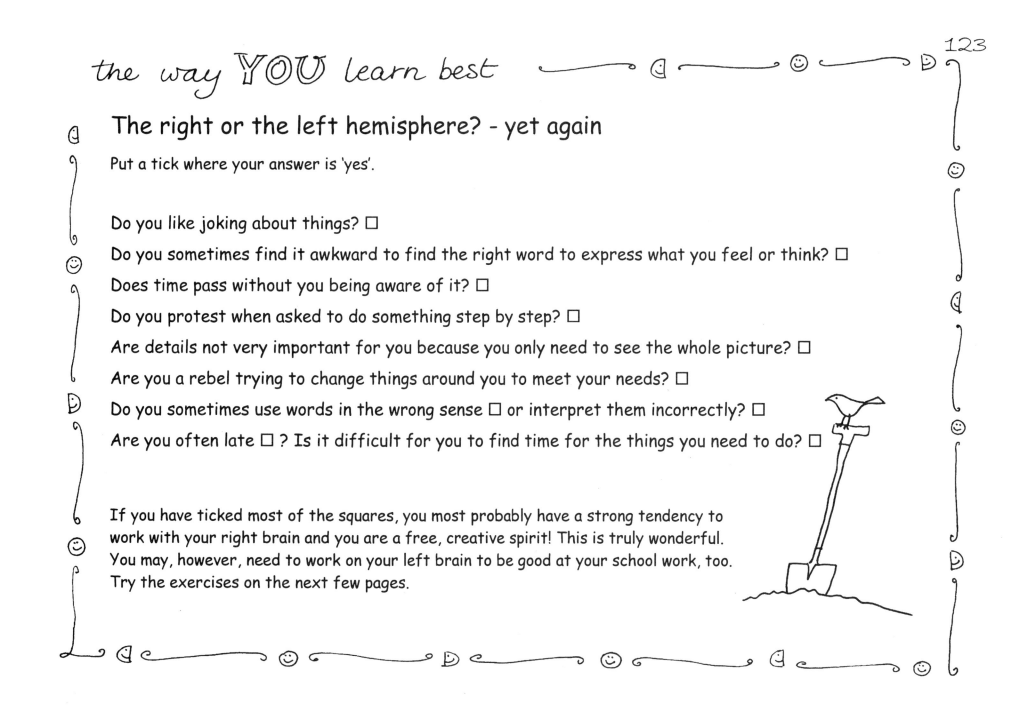

the way YOU learn best

Using your right hemisphere

Here are some ideas for you to try out if you want to exercise your right hemisphere, celebrate it, and use it to your advantage.

MOVE WHILE YOU LEARN

- swing your legs
- run, ride a bike or an exercise bike while listening to a taped lesson; you can use your head-phones!
- use big sheets of paper and write **big letters** when practising spelling
- bounce a ball repeating a memorised lesson

Think of other ways you can move while learning!

LISTEN TO SLOW CLASSICAL MUSIC when reading your textbook, learning something by heart, or solving problems.

the way YOU learn best

More ways of exercising your right hemisphere

Imagine in your head things you are reading or listening to. This will help you not only understand but also remember better.

Find models/examples, whenever possible. They will let you know what the final product is supposed to look like!

Use Mind Maps® for making notes and for taking notes. They are brilliant! (see next chapter)

Start by reading the final part of the text. It will be easier to understand what you are reading because you will have the big picture, which means you will know what the text is all about.

Use colour whenever you can. Use coloured pencils for marking and coloured paper for writing. Use colour for everything you need to remember!

the way YOU learn best

Advice for learners who learn best while moving and touching

If you are fed up sitting still at your desk, stand up, walk about, hold something in your hand (rolling, tapping or throwing it in the air). All this simply means that in order to learn well, you need to move.

It is not possible to jump, wave your arms or walk around in class, but at home you can easily see whether movement helps you learn.

Here are a few tips:

- stand up when you have to come up with ideas

- swing your legs while reading

- walk around the room or the garden reciting times-tables, or listening to the taped lesson on your walkman

- bounce a ball against the wall sounding difficult words, reciting a poem or revising your presentation.

Think of other ways you can move while learning.

ANY MOVEMENT IS GOOD AS LONG AS IT IS SAFE

the way YOU learn best

This is the way I learn best

Browse through the last twenty pages and complete the sentence:

To learn well and enjoy it, I ....

....

....

....

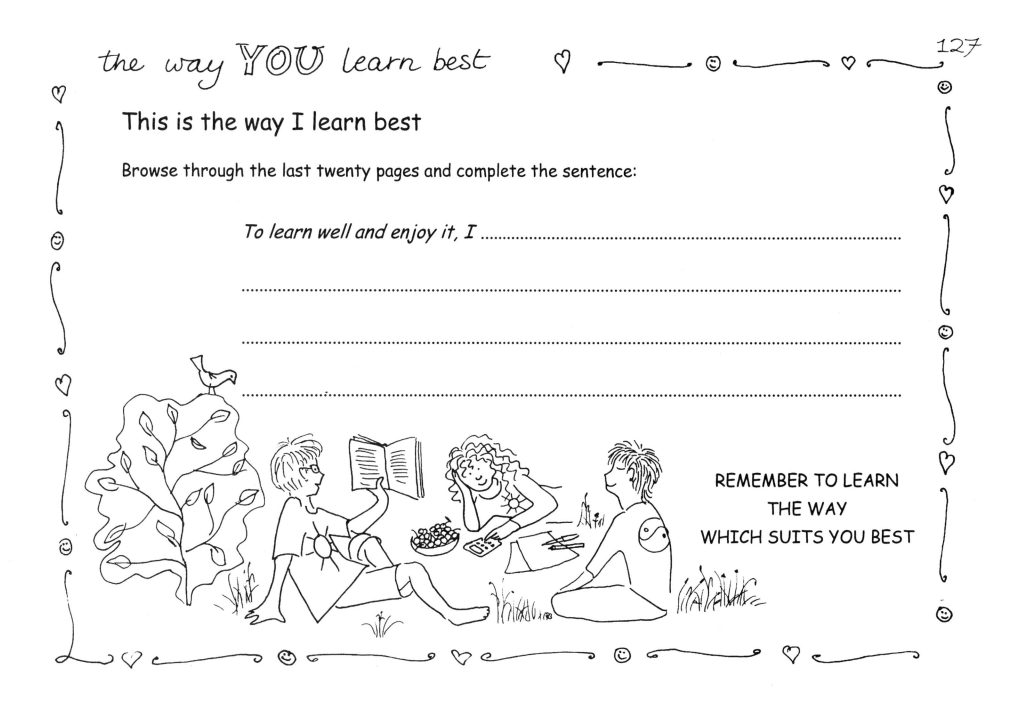

**REMEMBER TO LEARN
THE WAY
WHICH SUITS YOU BEST**

the way YOU learn best

Activating your neglected hemisphere

As you already know, one of your hemispheres may be more active than the other. If so, you can consciously use it to your advantage. However, it is important that the other one doesn't feel neglected and forgotten and that it gets some exercise, too. Only then will they be able to complement each other and work in harmony, making learning a happy and effective experience for you.

If your left hemisphere is very active, exercise your right one:

- make a plasticine model of a ship or a house

- sit on the floor, close your eyes, put your hand on your heart and think how you **feel**

- take some finger paints and make a big picture. Using your fingers cover the whole page with paints

- put on some music and dance expressing the music with your body

- go for a walk and notice all the beautiful plants

- take a picture of an animal and try to imagine its feelings.

If your right hemisphere is very active, exercise your left one:

- tidy up all your drawers

- make a simple model, e.g. a skeleton or an aeroplane, following written instructions

- find out how a clock, a washing machine or a bike pump work (any other machine will do, of course!), and explain it to a friend

- arrange your photographs putting them into an album in the right order (Summer holiday or school trip pictures will be fine)

- write an essay describing the photographed events

- always wear a watch and try to be punctual wherever you go.

the way YOU learn best

CROSS PAT and CROSS WALK

Here is a good way to activate both hemispheres at the same time.

Sit on a sofa or a chair.

Lift your right knee and pat it with your left hand.

Lift your left knee and pat it with your right hand.

Repeat slowly ten times.

When you have practised that for a while, do another exercise.

Stand up.

Lift your right knee and touch it with your left elbow.

Lift your left knee and touch it with your right elbow.

Repeat ten times, slowly and gracefully.

REMEMBER TO BREATHE AND DRINK WATER EVERY TIME YOU DO EXERCISES

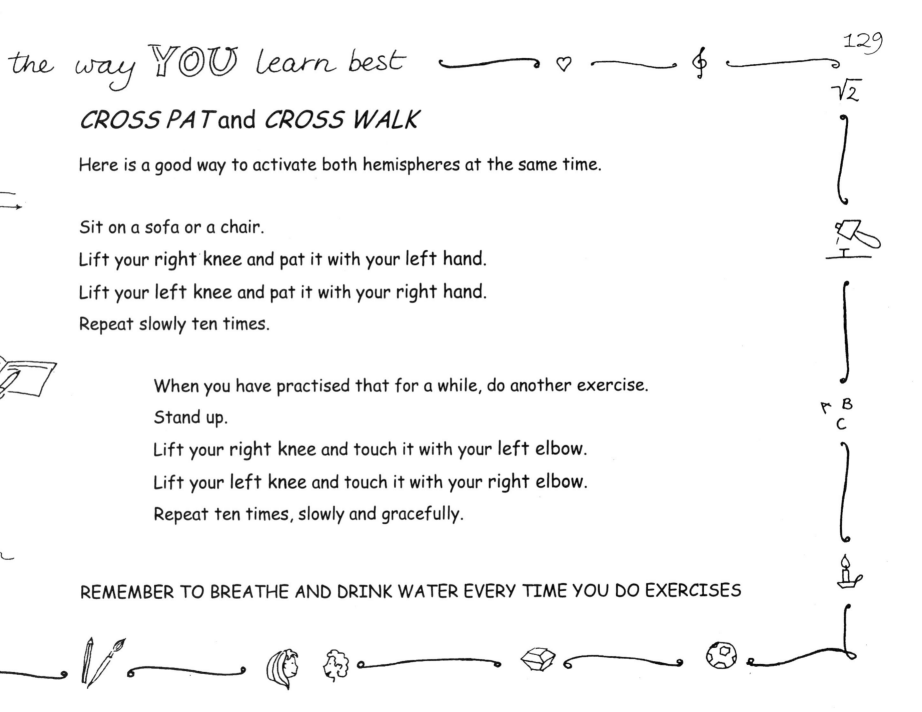

the way YOU learn best

Your many intelligences

Did you know that you have a number of different intelligences and not just one, as people used to believe (and many still do)?

All your intelligences are extremely important. Some are more important if you want to be an artist, some for good communication with people, and others to get high grades at school.

Some scientists have noticed that the intelligences we need for school work are not necessarily the ones which make us happy and successful in life. However, the best thing to do is to try to develop as many intelligences as you can, so that you can succeed in both: school and life.

Look at the picture on the next page and think:

- which are your best developed intelligences?
- which are OK?
- which need some work?
- which need a lot of work?

YOU CAN DEVELOP YOUR INTELLIGENCES IF YOU CHOOSE TO WORK ON THEM

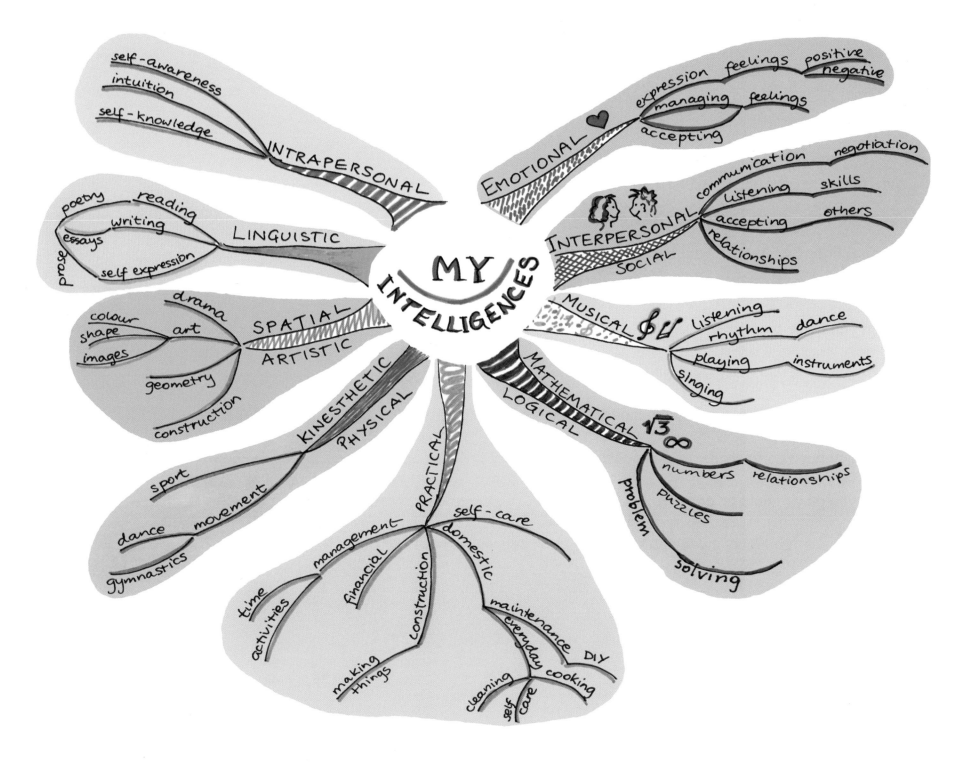

the way YOU learn best

More about your intelligences

We need different intelligences in different situations.
Which of your intelligences do you need the most:

when you draw pictures? ....

when you compose music and write lyrics? ....

when you want to put together a model aeroplane? ....

when you have to describe the process of making paper? ....

when you play tennis or dance? ....

when you control your anger and express your feelings without hurting the other person? ....

....

the way YOU learn best

And now think what you may need the following intelligences for:

Intrapersonal intelligence (your self-knowledge) ....

Linguistic intelligence ....

Spatial/Artistic intelligence ....

Kinesthetic intelligence ....

Mathematical/Logical intelligence ....

Musical/Rhythmic intelligence ....

Interpersonal intelligence (relating to others) ....

Emotional intelligence ....

TO BE INTELLIGENT MEANS TO DISCOVER ONE'S INTELLIGENCES
AND MAKE GOOD USE OF THEM

the way YOU learn best

Your body language and learning

Have you ever thought that your body language may affect your learning? Well, it certainly may! The posture your body assumes can strongly influence the way you feel in general and also how you feel about learning. If you feel positive and motivated, the results of your work have a good chance to be good!

Try an interesting experiment:

Slump in your chair and tilt your head down.

Stick out your lower lip and tense the muscles around your eyes.

Stay in this position and try to feel happy and optimistic. How is it going?

And now sit up straight. Head up, shoulders relaxed.

Lift the corners of your mouth and widen your eyes.

Stay like that and try to feel absolutely miserable. Is that possible?

Can you see how important it is to watch your body language?!

the way YOU learn best

Send your brain on holiday

Sometimes you may find yourself sitting at your desk and absent-mindedly gazing at the wall in front of you. There is so much homework for tomorrow but you just can't get started... You have tried everything: the relaxation and some energising exercises, which are supposed to help you focus your attention on the task in hand. Nothing has worked! What to do?

A BREAK! You simply need a break! Send your brain on holiday!

Look out of the window and daydream... Don't force your brain to do anything it doesn't want to do. Just let it be for a while... Go to the garden and bounce a ball or do a few roly-polys... After a while the brain will let you know that it doesn't need any more free time. Put on some classical music, fairly fast and loud and breathe it in. After 10-15 minutes of letting it be, your brain will be ready to get on with your homework.

Take a break every 30 - 45 minutes; this way your brain will run smoothly rather than getting overloaded and blocked.

BREAKS ARE VERY IMPORTANT!

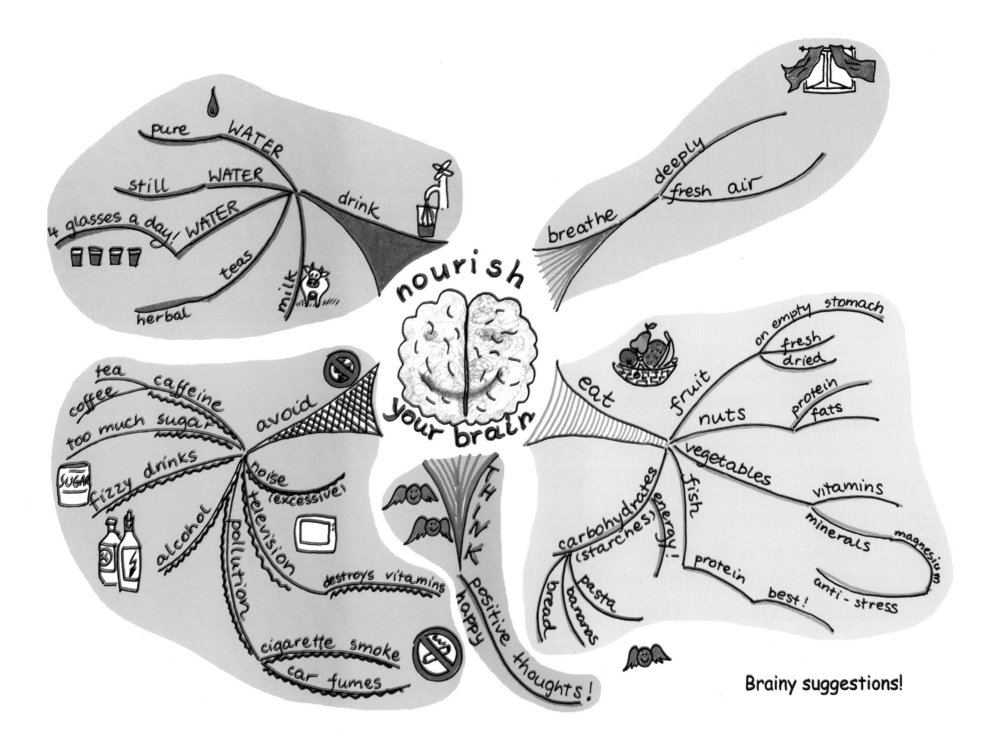

Brainy suggestions!

the way YOU learn best

Sum it all up

Go through the exercises in this chapter, marking all the important discoveries you have made about the way you learn best.

Then write about them here: ....

....

....

....

....

Now, take a large sheet of paper and write in the centre: THE BEST WAY I LEARN. Draw a few branches coming out of the centre and write on them all the things you want to remember. Let this sheet join the others already hanging on your wall.

It is necessary to read your notes every day for at least three weeks. After that you will still need to go through them from time to time to refresh your memory.

your magic learning tools

Learning with ease and joy? Great idea! But how to do it?

To do anything at all, first you have to have an idea. However, an idea is only the starting point. In order to put your idea into practice, you need to acquire the right kind of tools. The right tools make the job in hand not only possible but also much easier and more pleasant.

This is also true about learning. If you want your learning to be effective and enjoyable, you need to get yourself the right tools - some very specific ways which will help you do what you want to do.

This chapter will show you some learning tools from which you will be able to choose those that suit you best.

Have fun!

your magic learning tools

I have to read this. Very well, but what for?

Before you start reading a book, an article in a magazine or a brochure advertising new models of cars, ask yourself a question: *Why am I reading this?*

The way you read letters from your friend or an article in your favourite magazine is different from the way you read a novel, a textbook or the information telling you how to put a new programme into your computer.

Think for a moment: what are the possible reasons you read?

Now write down your ideas.

....

....

....

....

THE WAY YOU READ DEPENDS ON WHY YOU READ

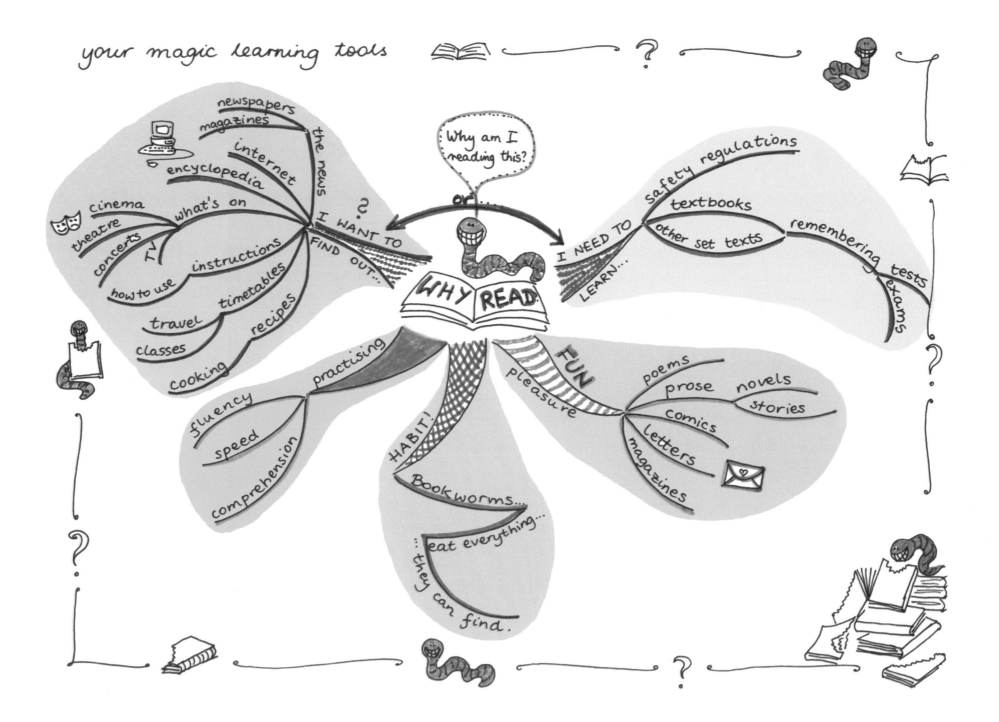

Different ways you read

Sometimes you read fast, not bothering to read every single word of the text. At other times you read slower, making sure you read every sentence on the page. Sometimes you pay attention to what you are reading, trying to remember as much as possible. At other times you just browse through the text noticing only things that interest you. And sometimes you read not thinking about the speed or about paying attention; you just enjoy being with the book and forget about the world around you.

Think and write how you will read:

♦ a magazine article that interests you ....

♦ a letter from your best friend ....

♦ a chapter in your geography book ....

♦ some information you have found in the encyclopedia or on the Internet ....

♦ a time table (your school lessons or trains) ....

♦ an entertainment guide ....

♦ a novel ....

♦ your own essay ....

Discuss with your friends the different ways of reading and see what they think.

Before you start reading

When you sit down (or lie down?) to read a chapter in your textbook or an article in a magazine, first:

- ◆ read the title, the subtitles and all the headings

- ◆ read everything written in **bold print** or *italics*

- ◆ look at the pictures, photographs, tables and graphs

- ◆ read a few sentences from the introduction and the last paragraph of the text.

This way you will know a lot about the text even before you start reading it.

Your new textbook - getting acquainted

When you meet people for the first time, there are some things you may want to know about them, like their names, where they live, what they like doing, what their interests are.

Getting acquainted with a new book is in some ways similar. There are some things that are good to know about a book before you start reading it.

How to get acquainted with a new book:

- look at the title, the subtitle and the name of the author

- browse through the book looking at pictures, photographs, tables, graphs, anything that stands out

- read the introduction

- see if there are any suggestions on how to use the book, any explanations of symbols and abbreviations,

- go to the end of the book and look for an index, a glossary, or any recommendations

- browse through the book again and stop whenever you see something of interest to you.

When you do all this, reading will be much, much easier because you will already know a lot about the content of the book.

MAKE SURE YOU DO ALL THAT BEFORE YOU START READING THE TEXT!

Making friends with your textbook

Sit comfortably and hold your book in both hands.

Close you eyes and weigh the book in your hands... is it light?... is it heavy?

Feel its thickness, the smoothness of its cover...

Holding the book in your hands imagine it becoming smaller... smaller... smaller...

So small that you can easily hold it in closed hands...

Sense the content of the book... all the interesting, maybe amusing things in it...

All the knowledge contained in the book is in your hands.

Say to your book: *You are interesting,*

easy to understand and fun to read!

Open your hands and let the book return to its original shape.

Open your eyes and smile at the book.

You have become friends!

What you see on the page

📖 Look at the sentence below.

READING IS EASY AND ENJOY(AB)LE. IT CAN BE FUN FOR YOU, TOO!

Fixing your eyes on the two circled letters, count how many more you can see to the right and left of the circle. Now holding the book in two hands, make it stand in front of you. Push it a little further away and fixing your eyes on the circle, count once again the letters you can see to the right and to the left of the circle.

Has the number changed? You can probably see more this way.

To read fluently you will have to see more than one word at a time; maybe two, three, or even four...

You already know one way to see more: push your book a little further away from your eyes and make it stand.

The next exercise will show you another way.

You could see more

Hold your hands 30cm in front of your eyes, your index fingertips touching.

Fix your gaze at the point where your fingertips touch.

Now wriggling your fingers, slowly pull your hands horizontally away from each other.

Holding your head absolutely still, watch the wriggling fingers moving away.

When you cannot see them any more, stop.

Do this exercise every time you intend to read something.

It will not only help you read faster but it will also improve your eyesight!

Your little helpers:

a finger, a pencil, a ruler

When you read without a guide, your eyes can easily go off the line and wander all over the page, making many unnecessary movements.

The most obvious guide-pointer is your own finger. Move it smoothly along the line of the text to read faster and more fluently.

Try this experiment:

Sit in front of a friend. Ask him to 'draw' circles with his eyes without moving his head. Watch the movement of his eyes very carefully. Has he been able to 'draw' smooth circles?

Now 'draw' circles in the air with your finger and ask your friend to follow your fingertip with his eyes. Can you see the difference?

You must have noticed how much easier it is to 'draw' circles with your eyes following the movement of a finger.

USING POINTERS HELPS YOU READ FASTER AND MORE FLUENTLY

Reading is a wonderful thing to do

Especially when it is easy and when what we read is really interesting.

The trouble is that for most of us the only way to make reading easy and fun is by... reading, reading, and more reading!

When you practise reading

- find books which really interest you

- find your favourite reading position:

    lying on your tummy on the floor,

    sitting on a cushion, on the carpet, on a chair at the table, on a sofa

- try holding the book vertically in front of you

- try reading through a sheet of transparent plastic in your favourite colour.

- always make sure that the light is good!

And one more thing: while you read, hold your left ankle with your right hand.

Does it sound like magic? Well, just try it and see whether it helps!

Letters: big or small?

Many people who are not very keen on reading (because they haven't mastered it yet!) often prefer books with letters bigger than average. It might be a good idea to find out what size of letters is best for you and then try to find books printed that way.

<small>Do you like letters that small?</small>

Is this better at all?

How about letters this size?

I suppose these are big enough!

Not to mention this size.

Which size of letters do you like best?

Many libraries store books printed in big letters. Try to make sure that the print you read is the best possible you can find. When your reading becomes more fluent, you will feel more comfortable with smaller print as well. You may also need to have your eyes tested, just in case...

IF THE PRINT IS TOO SMALL FOR YOU,

USE A **MAGNIFYING GLASS!**

your magic learning tools

How to read,

so that you can remember

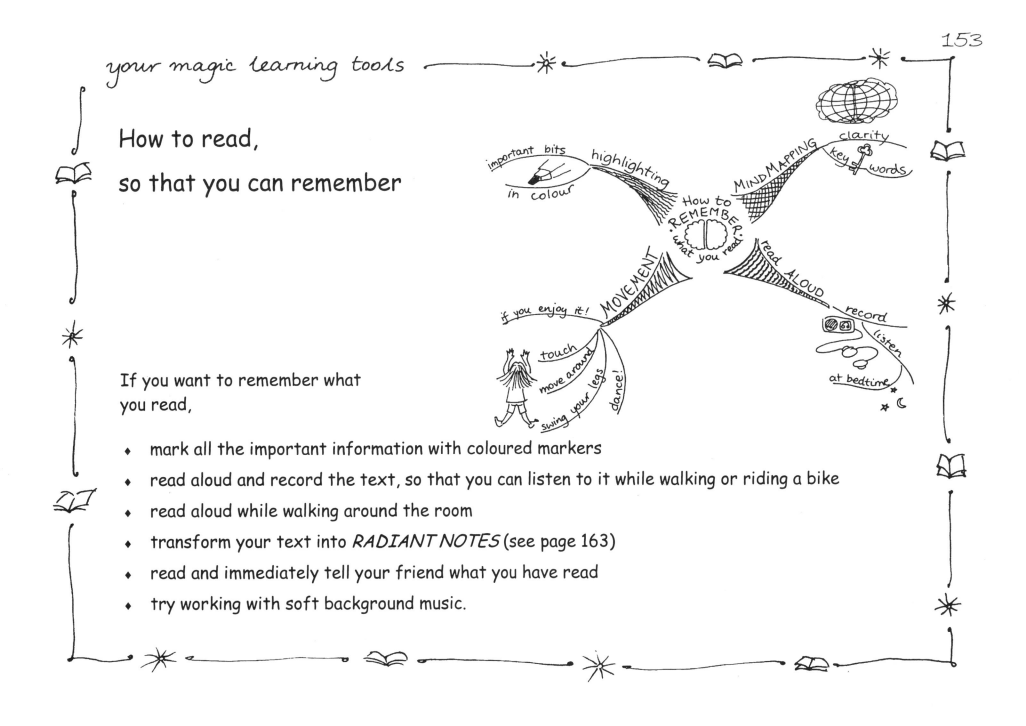

If you want to remember what you read,

- mark all the important information with coloured markers
- read aloud and record the text, so that you can listen to it while walking or riding a bike
- read aloud while walking around the room
- transform your text into *RADIANT NOTES* (see page 163)
- read and immediately tell your friend what you have read
- try working with soft background music.

Remember, remember

Do you realise how many things you already remember? Your brain stores thousands and thousands of pieces of information, much more than you can even begin to imagine.

There is always a need to remember something new: a friend's telephone number, your teacher's face, times-tables, the spelling of long and seemingly hard words, the time your favourite TV programme comes on, and many, many other things.

You will remember without much effort:

- something at the beginning of a lesson, a text or a TV programme
- something you hear at the end
- something repeated a number of times
- something connected with another thing you already know
- something that surprises, maybe even shocks you
- something that is really very interesting to you.

Remember, remember

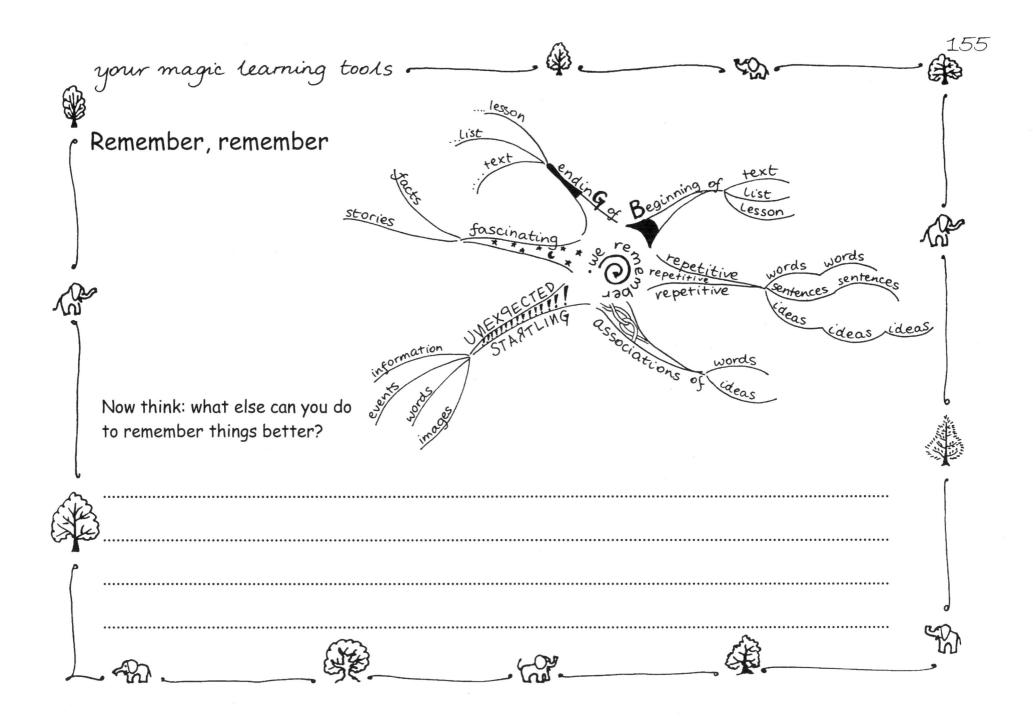

Now think: what else can you do
to remember things better?

....

....

....

....

Words flow swiftly... straight onto paper

There is a notebook on your desk in front of you and the title of a composition on the top of a page. That's all... the rest of the page is empty. You've been sitting, looking at it for quite a while but nothing, not a single idea what to write comes to mind.

It's getting late... what to do?!

A *HELICOPTER SPIN* might be a good start,

massaging your *BRAIN BUTTONS* could be useful.

When you have done that, try *SWIFTWRITING*.

SWIFTWRITING

Set a timer for 10 minutes.

Start writing and write... write... write...

Write as quickly as you can, whatever comes to mind, even if you think what you're writing doesn't make much sense. Ignore any mistakes you make on the way, just continue writing. Don't stop, not even for a moment, until the time is up.

Now read what you have written and see how much of it you can use in your composition. Re-write it, making necessary changes, re-arranging the order where necessary, and correcting your spelling.

Brief or elaborate?

Many people write very brief compositions because they seem to be lacking ideas about what more they could write. However, it may be necessary to learn to write more because not many teachers will accept a few lines as a full length composition! What to do to make your compositions longer and more complete?

Here is an idea for you to try out.

FACTS and DESCRIPTIONS

FACT	DESCRIPTION (questions)	
Yesterday we went to the park.	What time of day was it?	Did you meet anybody you know?
	Who went to the park?	What did you do in the park?
	What was the park like?	How long were you there?
	What did you see there?	Did you enjoy your walk?
	Any animals? Interesting plants?	Are you thinking of going there again?

Answering the questions you can write a long enough composition about yesterday's walk.

Start writing and **don't stop** until you finish. Only then you can correct your mistakes.

Change facts into descriptions

FACT

DESCRIPTION (write questions)

Our team has won the match

....

....

....

....

I love animals

....

....

....

....

Now write a composition on one of the topics, answering the questions you have asked yourself.

Writing tells a story

Think about something amusing that has happened to you or something funny you have witnessed.

> Bring the whole situation back to mind.
>
> See it clearly and in colour...
>
> Hear the sounds you heard when it happened.
>
> Remember what happened before? And after?

Now imagine that you are telling your friend about the event but the words, instead of coming out of your mouth, slide down your pen and stay on paper. Write as fast as you can until the whole story is finished.

After you have finished, correct any mistakes you may have made, make changes and re-arrange the parts.

Writing tells more stories

Add more stories to the one in which you have described an amusing event.

Here are some more ideas of what to write about:

- a sad moment in your life
- something that made you very angry
- the happiest moment you can remember
- your extraordinary adventure.

The stories may be true or imagined, whichever you like. Just remember:

- bring the situation to mind, imagining it very clearly and in colour
- hear the sounds, smell the scents, and feel the touch
- add what happened before and after the event.

Imagine telling somebody your stories while you write.

When all the stories are ready, check the spelling of the words you are not sure about. Then ask an adult to type them on the computer (unless you can do it yourself!) and to print them out. Draw pictures for every story, and remember to make a cover page with the title and the name of the author: your name!

How does it feel to have written a book?

How do you spell this word???

Spelling can be a real nuisance... Learning to spell correctly takes many of us a long, long time (we have other talents, though!) but in the end everyone can improve their spelling, if only they want to.

If hearing or touch are your preferred senses, you can use them to help you get the spelling right.

Think of a word you have recently spelled incorrectly. Take some finger paints in your favourite colours. Dip your fingertips in one of them and looking at the correctly written word, write it with your fingers on a large sheet of paper. Wash the paint off your fingers. Close your eyes and 'write' the same word in the air.

Open your eyes to look once more at the correctly spelled word and closing your eyes 'write' it in the air. Now do the same thing with your eyes open.

Finally, covering the word, write it once more, this time on paper.

Every time you are not sure how to spell a word, do this exercise. Sometimes it takes many repetitions, but in the end you will get it right!

On the lines or radiantly?

School notebooks usually have lines, along which we arrange our thoughts. It is similar to arranging books on shelves. This way you may store quite a number in a relatively small space.

Could you tell how your thoughts are arranged in your brain?

They seem to be all over the place, certainly not in lines!
Tony Buzan invented Mind Maps® which best reflect the way our brain works.

When you first start using mind mapping, you may find it awkward, strange or silly. However, your brain will soon start enjoying the radiant notes and will get used to them faster than you think. This is what your brain feels most comfortable with!

Many people who use mind mapping believe that it is an absolutely brilliant learning tool, one of the best ever invented. It will help you discover the true joy of learning every time you prepare for a test, make a essay plan, write a summary, think of new ideas or take notes from a talk. Your work will be easier, much more enjoyable, you will be able to do it much faster and have more time for other things.

Making radiant notes

Our brains don't think in lines; they think in a radiant way. Radiant notes are in harmony with the natural way the brain works.

In this book you have already seen a few of those.
Now is the time for you to make them yourself.

your magic learning tools

Take a sheet of blank paper and put it on its side, like this: ☐

In the centre of the sheet write your **topic** or draw a **picture** symbolizing your topic.

Draw **thick branches** coming out of the centre. They may be wavy, just like branches of a tree, or straight, whichever you prefer.

Using only **key words** (the most important words) write on the bare branches all ideas that come to your mind in connection with the topic. Write the words in capital letters.

Now draw **thinner branches** coming out of the thick ones and write on them whatever comes to mind in connection with the words/ideas written on the thick branches.

Write **anything that comes to mind**: what you think and what you feel. All ideas are important and you can never tell which ones will eventually be better or more original.

Use **the same colour marker** for every thick branch and its thinner branches.
Use different colours for different branches.

Print the words or **write very clearly** (in the same colour) to make your notes clearer and prettier.

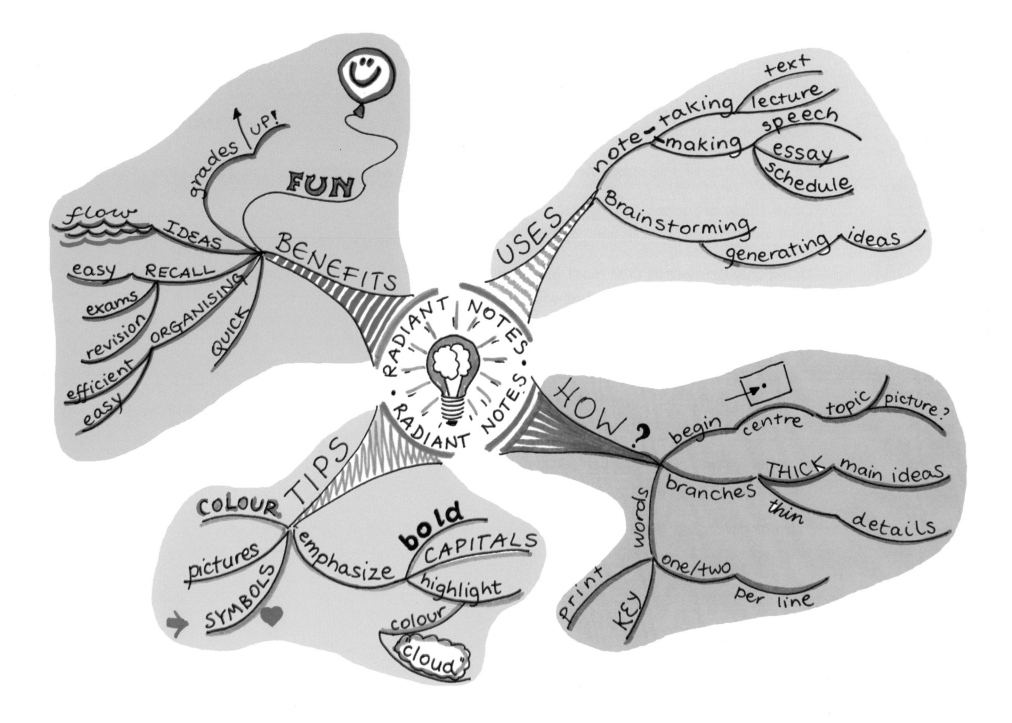

your magic learning tools

Let's practise making radiant notes

The mind map on the next page is about your school. We have started it for you by drawing the thick branches and writing on them the key words representing your sub-topics. Write on the thin branches all the details connected with the given key words.

For example, look at the branch with the word LESSONS written on it and write anything that comes to mind: long or short, boring or interesting, English, maths, P.E., too many, your favourite, and so on.

When you have completed the whole map, write an essay about your school, making use of the information you have on your branches.

The ideas belonging to each main branch and its thin branches will be turned into one paragraph in your essay.

your magic learning tools

My School

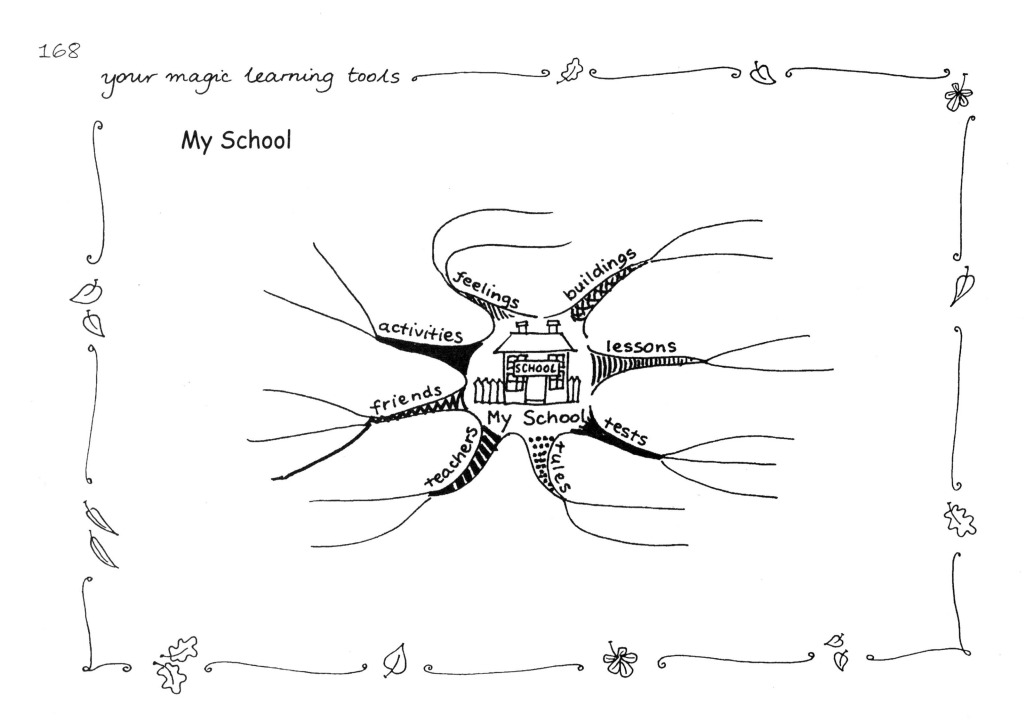

Mind-Notes and Heart-Notes

Our feelings are as important as our thoughts. Your radiant notes should include both, the feelings and the thoughts.

To show the importance of feelings, we would like you to do a special exercise.

Here, the first 'map' about your family will be your 'thought' map, the second will show only how you feel.

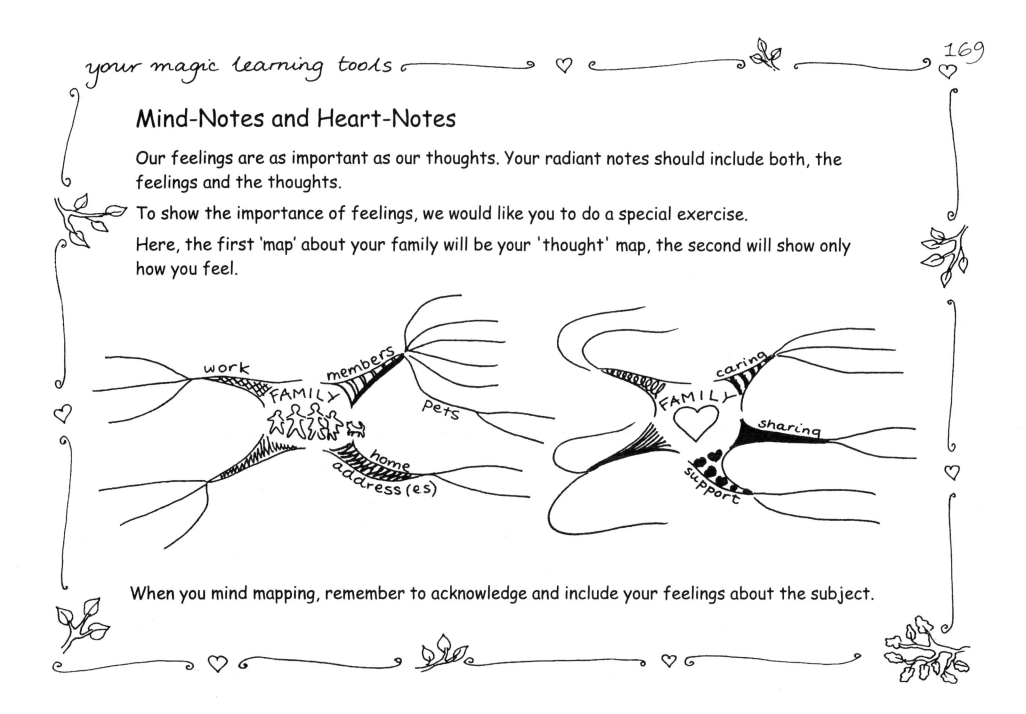

When you mind mapping, remember to acknowledge and include your feelings about the subject.

your magic learning tools

From radiant notes to an essay

Make radiant notes about YOU on the next page.

On the lines write everything about you and your life: the important people, your likes and dislikes, your characteristics and interests, your routines, plans for the future, and anything else that comes to mind.

When you have finished filling the lines with words, look at your notes and think: *If I were to talk about myself, what would I talk about first, second, third...* Put numbers on the lines in the order you think is right.

Now start writing your essay; each main line together with its thinner lines will create one paragraph.

Write without stopping until you describe what is on all the lines.

Now read your composition, add anything you may have forgotten to write about and correct your mistakes.

You can give it to your Mum or to your best friend to read.

Maybe your teacher would like to read it, too?

your magic learning tools

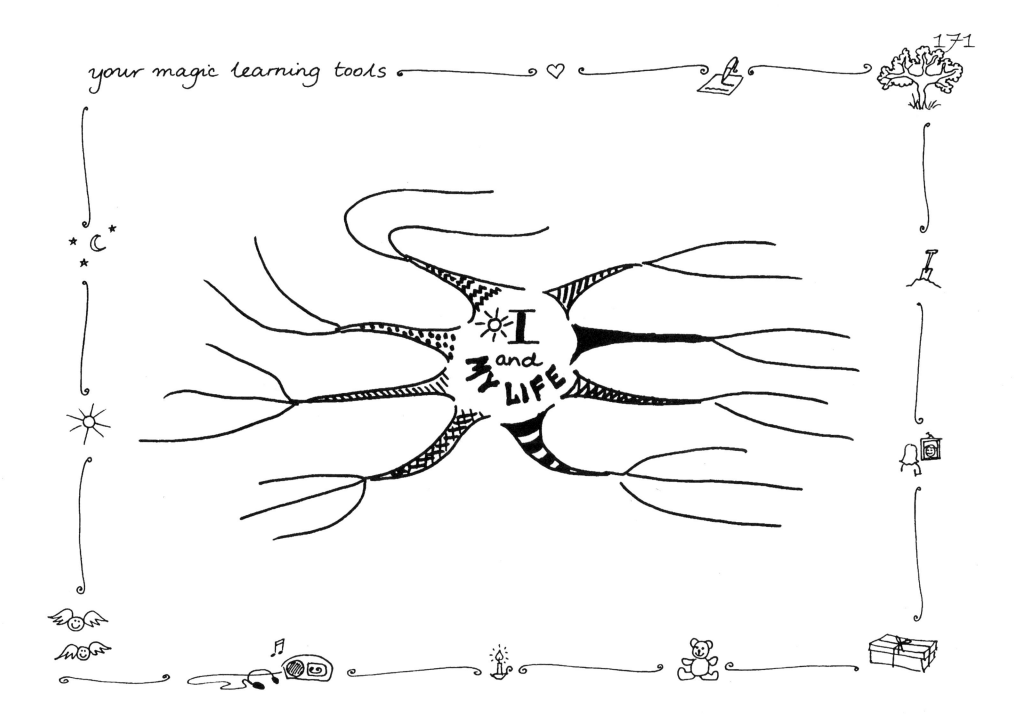

I and MY LIFE

your magic learning tools

Transforming a story into radiant notes

Read a short story and write a summary in the form of radiant notes.

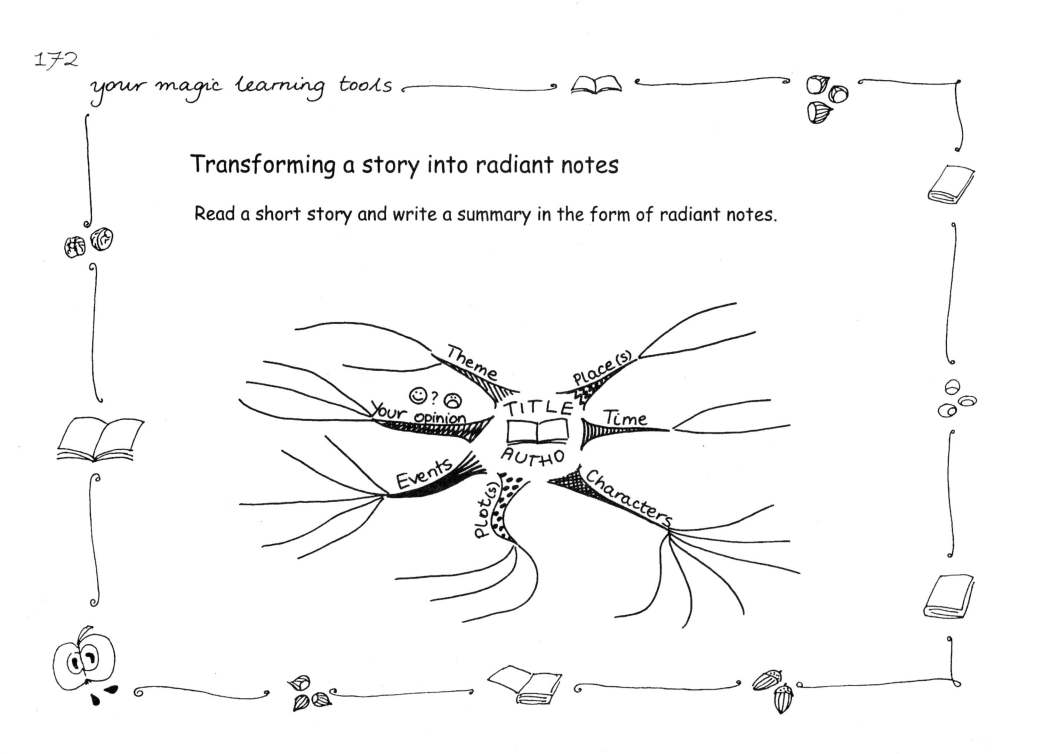

Radiant notes and preparing for a test

Write your revision topic in the centre of a page.
You may want to draw a picture representing the topic.

Look through the notes in your notebook or find the right chapter in the book.
What are the sub-topics?
Write them on the thick lines coming out of the centre.

Add details on the thin lines attached to the main ones while reading your notes.
You may need to draw little twigs attached to the thin lines to add more details.

Remember:

Use a different colour for each thick line and its thinner lines.

Print the words carefully (CAPITAL LETTERS) or write clearly.

Printing and colouring will make remembering much easier.

your magic learning tools

Sum it all up

What are the three most important things you have learned about reading?

1. .... 2. .... 3. ....

And the three most important things you have learned about writing?

1. .... 2. .... 3. ....

What are the most important things you want to remember?

1. .... 2. .... 3. ....

4. .... 5. ....

Make a mind map showing all the learning tools you want to use and remember about. In the centre of a page write: MY LEARNING TOOLS. Draw as many lines as you need and fill them with key words and pictures.

Put the radiant notes on your wall to join the others.

that's it for now!

The closing exercise

You have completed your first journey to the land of joyful and effective learning.

Now the thing to do is to go through your 'Sum it all up' radiant note posters from all five chapters every day for three weeks without fail! This will give you a perfect chance to ensure that what you have discovered becomes an important part of your life and learning.

When the three weeks are over, take the five posters off the wall. Get one last large sheet of paper, this time combining all the information on one sheet. Make it really special: write very clearly, draw as many pictures as you can and use coloured markers.

Let this note radiate on your wall until you undertake another similar journey towards self-discovery.

We would be delighted to hear your comments about the exercises and how you got on with them.

Please, do write to us! Our address is:

Eva Hoffman and Zdzislaw Bartkowicz

Learn to Learn
PO Box 29
Middlewich
Cheshire CW10 9FN
United Kingdom

Bibliography for teachers and parents

Among the many wonderful books about learning, here are the ones we found particularly useful:

Beaver, Diana. LAZY LEARNING. Element Books Ltd. England (1994)

Brewer, Chris and Campbell, Don G. RHYTHMS OF LEARNING. Zephyr Press, Arizona (1991)

Buzan, Tony. THE MIND MAP® BOOK. BBC Books, England. (1990)

Childre, Doc Lew. TEACHING CHILDREN LOVE. Planetary Publications. California (1996)

Dennison, Paul E. and Dennison Gail E. BRAIN GYM®. (Teachers's edition revised)
     Edu-Kinesthetics, Inc. Ventura, California (1994)

De Porter, Bobbi. QUANTUM LEARNING. Piatkus (1993)

Dryden, Gordon and Dr Vos, Jeannette. THE LEARNING REVOLUTION.
     Accelerated LEARNING Systems. Unwin Brothers, England (1994)

Goelitz, Jeffrey. THE ULTIMATE KID. University of the Trees Press. California (1986)

Hannaford, Carla. SMART MOVES. Great Ocean Publishers. Virginia (1995)

Kline, Peter. THE EVERYDAY GENIUS. Great Ocean Publishers. Virginia (1988)

McPhee, Doug. LIMITLESS LEARNING. Zephyr Press. Arizona (1996)

Meister Vitale, Barbara. UNICORNS ARE REAL. Jalmar Press, California (1982)

Meister Vitale, Barbara. FREE FLIGHT. CELEBRATING YOUR RIGHT BRAIN. Jalmar Press, California (1986)

Mosley, Jenny. CIRCLE TIME. Nasen Publication. England (1996)

O'Brien, Jonathan. LIGHTNING LEARNING. Quantum Training UK Ltd. (1998)

Olivier, Carolyn and Bowler, Rosemary F. LEARNING TO LEARN. Simon and Schuster. New York (1996)

Rose, Colin. ACCELERATED LEARNING. Topaz Publishing Limited. England (1985)

Rozman, Deborah. MEDITATING WITH CHILDREN. Planetary Publications, California (1994)

Sims, Pamela. AWAKENING BRILLIANCE. Bayhampton Publications, Canada, (1997)

White, Murray. SELF ESTEEM. ITS MEANING AND VALUE AT SCHOOLS. Daniels Publishers, England (1996)

Acknowledgements:

Our great thanks go to the authors to whom we are particularly indebted, whose ideas we have used and transformed into our exercises:

Tony Buzan and all his *Mind Mapping* books:
thank you, Tony, for this most brilliant learning/teaching tool! We use it all the time.

Murray White's books and his wonderful workshops have inspired the *Smile at yourself* section of this workbook.

Gordon Dryden's and Jeannette Vos's mine of information contained in *The Learning Revolution* has all been of enormous value to us!

Doc Lew Childre's *Teaching Children Love*:
we have drawn on his ideas in exercises pp. 10, 79, 97, and 101.

Paul and Gail Dennison's *Brain Gym* and Carla Hannaford's *Smart Moves* inspired exercises on pp. 80, 95, 98, 99, and 129.
We have changed some of the original names of the 'moves', as suggested by children.

Bobbi de Porter's *Quantum Learning* has been wonderfully informative and helped us greatly with exercises on pp. 122, 123, 134, and 156.

Barbara Meister Vitale's *Unicorns Are Real* and *Free Flight* have been a true inspiration for pp. 93, 102, 124, 125 and 126.

Dr. Eva Hoffman started her teaching career over thirty years ago teaching young children English as a foreign language, designing her own programmes and materials. As a university lecturer and a teacher educator she has been passionately studying and promoting learning skills while teaching EFL and English for academic purposes, lecturing in methodology of teaching, educational and developmental psychology, and music. Eva has been developing learning skills programmes for children and young people and now runs LEARN TO LEARN workshops for children, teachers and parents, in the UK and abroad.

Dr. Zdzislaw Bartkowicz is a professor of psycho-pedagogy at the University MCS in Lublin, Poland. For many years he has been researching the re-socialising effects of psychotherapy, as well as specialising in the application of psychotherapy in education.

Zdzislaw has vast experience as a lecturer and a psychotherapist. Fascinated with the beneficial effects of music therapy combined with deep relaxation and visualisation on learning, he composes his own music using it in courses and workshops for children and their parents, teachers, and teacher trainers.

" We are convinced that every child has enormous potential for learning and is capable of making remarkable progress. If this is not happening, it is most probably because we, the children's teachers, have not yet found the right keys to their hearts and minds. This book is an attempt to find those unique keys that will unlock their unlimited potential."

(E. Hoffman and Z. Bartkowicz)

#	Track	Time
1	Relaxation exercise - introduction *	1' 19"
2	Deep relaxation exercise	15' 07"

J. S. Bach - music for flute and piano **

3	Arioso, Concerto in A	5' 25"
4	Siciliano, Sonata in Eb	2' 08"
5	Largo ma non tanto, Concerto in d	5' 40"
6	Air, Suite in D	4' 14"
7	Adagio, Sonata in C	1' 37"
8	Affettuoso, Brandenburg Concerto No.5 in D	5' 12"
9	Siciliano, Sonata in E	3' 22"
10	Andante, Sonata in e	3' 42"
11	Aria, Cantata BWV 208	5' 42"

W. A. Mozart - Sonata in F, K.V. 13 ***

#	Track	Time
12	Allegro	2' 53"
13	Andante	3' 56"
14	Menuetto I & II	2' 21"

W. A. Mozart - Sonata in C, K.V. 14 ***

#	Track	Time
15	Allegro	5' 09"
16	Allegro	2' 22"
17	Menuetto I & II	2' 45"

Total time: 73' 04"

The Learning Adventure
companion CD
R.2

*   Exercise - Z. Bartkowicz, E. Hoffman ©
Music - *Ocean of Calm* by Z. Bartkowicz
Voice - Sarah Bull

**   Flute - Martin Hoffman
        & Sarah Bull (5, 8 & 11)
Piano - Marek Mietelski
        & Stephen Reynolds (10)

***   Flute - Martin Hoffman
Piano - Stephen Reynolds